M000290915

More INVENTION MYSTERIES

52 little-known true stories behind well-known inventions

by Paul Niemann
illustrations by Kevin Cordtz

MORE INVENTION MYSTERIES
52 little-known true stories behind well-known inventions

by Paul Niemann

Published by:
Horsefeathers Publishing Company
P.O. Box 5148
Quincy, IL 62305
www.InventionMysteries.com

All rights reserved. No part of this book may be reproduced or transmitted in any form without written permission from the author.

Copyright © 2006 Paul Niemann
Printed in the United States of America
Illustrations by Kevin Cordtz
Book layout and typesetting by Julie Hardison

Niemann, Paul
More Invention Mysteries: 52 little-known true stories behind well-known inventions / Paul Niemann. – 1st ed.
P.cm.
Includes bibliographic references and index.

ISBN 10: 0-9748041-1-8
ISBN 13 :978- 0-9748041-1-8

1. Inventions
2. Inventors
3. Mysteries

Acknowledgements:

☀ To my publicist, Leanne Hobbs, for her dedication and professionalism

☀ To Jessica Summers, for her contributions in researching the stories in this book

☀ To the newspaper editors who carry the *Invention Mysteries* syndicated column in their newspapers each week

☀ To Julie Barron, for her contributions in finding new markets for both *Invention Mysteries* books

☀ To the 22 students in Mrs. Terwelp's 5th grade class at St. Mary Grade School in Quincy, Illinois, for helping proofread the book

☀ To you, the reader

☀ And most importantly, to my parents, Ferd & Rita Niemann, for everything.

About the author

Paul Niemann's interest in inventions goes all the way back to his sophomore year in high school, when he saw two hot new inventions hit the market that year: the Trivial Pursuit game and spandex shorts. Those inventions made him dream of someday inventing a product that everyone wants. In 1998, Paul did just that when he invented the Impeachment Card Game.

The idea for the *Invention Mysteries* series was born when Paul was writing a how-to column for *Inventors' Digest* magazine. He then created his own weekly newspaper column, called *Invention Mysteries*, and began syndicating it. *More Invention Mysteries* is based on Paul's weekly newspaper column, and is a sequel to the first *Invention Mysteries* book.

Paul also teaches marketing and entrepreneurship at Quincy (IL) University, and he can be reached at niemann7@aol.com. Thanks for reading, and enjoy learning about the "little-known stories behind well-known inventions." We'll do it again next year.

"To invent, you need a good imagination
and a pile of junk,"
– Thomas Edison

Contents

What kept these inventors from obtaining patents on their own?

Chelsea Lannon invented a diaper with a pocket to hold a baby wipe and baby powder, but she couldn't get a patent without some help.

The Thompson sisters, Theresa and Mary, invented a solar teepee and called it a "Wigwarm." Pretty clever name, but the sisters weren't able to get a patent on their own.

Suzanna Goodin invented an edible spoon-shaped cracker. She even won a grand prize for her invention yet she, too, needed some help to get a patent.

Why couldn't these young women get patents on their own? Was it because property laws prevented women from owning property, including patents, during part of the 1700's and 1800's?

No, because all of the above inventors were born in the 1900's. Besides, inventor Robert Patch had the same problem as the other four inventors. So did Brandon Whale and his brother, Spencer, when they invented separate devices to help hospital patients.

Why, then, couldn't these inventors receive patents on their own?

It was because they weren't even 10 years old yet!

Young Ms. Lannon was only eight years old when she invented the diaper with a pocket in 1994, and the Thompson sisters were only eight and nine when they invented their solar teepee in 1960. Miss Goodin was only six when she invented her prize-winning edible spoon-shaped cracker.

Robert Patch was only six in 1963 when he received a patent for a toy truck that could be changed into different types of trucks.

Brandon Whale invented the "PaceMate" in 1998 to improve the electrical conductivity of his mother's sensor-bracelets after she had an operation for a pacemaker implant. His brother, Spencer, created a device to attach IV's to the wheeled vehicles that child patients rode in, allowing the IV's to stay in place.

In the end, each of these young inventors, except the Whale brothers, received patents for their great ideas.

By comparison, how old were some of the more famous inventors when they first achieved success?

Thomas Edison was 21 when he received his first patent, which was for a vote counter intended to speed things up in Congress. Despite the benefits it offered, it never made it onto the market.

Margaret Knight was 30 when she invented the machine that makes square-bottom paper bags in 1871, and that type of bag is still being used today. Alexander Graham Bell was 29 when he invented the telephone in 1876. Mattel co-founder Ruth Handler was 43 years old when she introduced the world to the Barbie Doll in 1959.

The United States Patent Office does not have an age requirement for receiving a patent. Most inventors, though, whether they're six or 60, need the assistance of a patent attorney to either prepare their patent application or at least review it before submitting it to the Patent Office. And most child inventors need to get some parental assistance when paying for the patent application and attorney fees.

Would you believe … that you can make an airplane out of that?

A robot that's more intelligent than its fellow agents … an agent who has a shoe with a phone built into it … a superhero who doesn't use a gun but can make an airplane out of just a few items like a fan, wooden poles and duct tape. Does it get any better than this?

Growing up in the '70s and '80s watching *Get Smart* re-runs and the hour-long *MacGyver* series, there were plenty of gadgets, contraptions and inventions to entertain us on TV. Let's take a look at the characters who relied on these gadgets to foil the bad guys.

"Sorry about that, Chief"

Armed with devices such as a shoe phone, a detonating pen that activated all the booby traps in his apartment, and the cone of silence for top-secret discussions with the chief of CONTROL (which is not an acronym), along with other inventions too numerous to list here, the bumbling Agent 86, a.k.a. Maxwell Smart, had a high-tech advantage over the evil agents of KAOS (also not an acronym).

One of the better contraptions on the show was Hymie, the human-like robot built by KAOS. Hymie once kidnapped Max and Agent 99, but soon released them and defected over to CONTROL because they treated him better than KAOS did. Hymie was equipped with a TV camera, a built-in computer, a calculator bank and a photocopy machine.

But this show was about more than just clever gadgets. Like much of what comes out of Hollywood, there are some interesting stories behind the show. For example, ABC had a chance to air the show but rejected it. NBC then picked it up on the condition that one of their own guys, Don Adams, play Maxwell Smart. After four seasons, NBC dropped it and CBS picked it up for a fifth and final season.

Maxwell Smart's love interest, Agent 99, never revealed her name on the show. After they married and had twins, their twins' names were kept secret, too. The reason probably had something to do with being in the spy business.

"With this paper clip and that empty gas can, you've got all the ingredients for a home-made bomb"

OK, so MacGyver never really said that, but he did invent some pretty clever ways to get out of a jam using only a few basic items plus his science background and a creative mind.

MacGyver could have used a gun to foil the bad guys like most action heroes do, but a childhood shooting accident resulted in him detesting guns. Instead, he chose to use his Swiss Army Knife, duct tape and any other items that were available to him at the time (such as a paper clip). The informal MacGyver had the unofficial title of "troubleshooter" while working for the mythical Phoenix Foundation.

MacGyver had his share of quirks, too. He was afraid of heights, and he always shook his hand in pain after punching one of the bad guys – you don't see many action heroes do that on TV. Like Agent 99, he also kept his first name secret; his friends usually referred to him as Mac. Even a college class picture referred to him by his last name only. During the seventh and final season, a dream revealed that MacGyver's first name was Angus, which is probably why he used only his last name.

As a result of losing his parents and grandmother in a car accident as a child, MacGyver was reluctant to get involved in serious relationships because he feared that he would lose anyone who got too close to him. In the series' final episode, though, he learned that he had a teenage son, making it possible for a future MacGyver series starring the young Sean Angus MacGyver, or "Sam" for short.

Hmmm. The stars of both series have given us replacements for a future generation of crime fighters. Could we see more human-like robots and homemade airplanes in the future? Stay tuned.

What inventions have come from Iraq?

Let's take a look at a few inventions whose origins trace back to Iraq – before it was known as Iraq.

While Iraq isn't known for having a rich history of inventions, it is the birthplace of many of the world's most important inventions and developments – some of which are taken for granted – such as streets and canals, as well as the first city-states around 3,500 B.C.

The area known today as Iraq was once known as Mesopotamia. That means that the country known now for its mass burial graves and possible weapons of mass destruction was once home to the Tower of Babel, was perhaps home to Noah's Ark and was probably home to the Garden of Eden.

The name Mesopotamia means "land between the two rivers" – the Tigris and Euphrates rivers – while Iraq is an Arab name which means "the shore and grazing area of a river." Mesopotamia is known as the "Cradle of Civilization," and its people were the first to record history in writing.

The southern part of Mesopotamia was known as Sumer, and it was this region which produced many of Mesopotamia's great innovations. The earliest known wheel was developed here around 3,000 B.C. and was soon used for chariots (the flat tire wasn't invented for another 4,900 years). It is possible that the wheel was originally developed somewhere else, as there were no written records prior to that point in time.

Sumerians developed the world's first form of writing, called Cuneiform, around 3,000 B.C., which was before the Egyptians developed hieroglyphics. Cuneiform contained more than 2,000 symbols and was written on clay tablets, and the scribes who could read and write were nearly always assured of a job because merchants, priests and judges needed someone to write and read their records for them.

Southern Mesopotamia was also home to the Biblical figure Abraham, and it was here that the Dead Sea Scrolls were discovered in 1947. The people of this region were excellent mathematicians and they based their math on the number 60 and in numbers that divide evenly into 60. This is where the 60-second minute, the 12-hour clock and the 360-degree circle all come from. Modern astrology even traces its roots back to the Mesopotamian people, as they used the location of the stars to schedule the planting of their crops.

Heading north, the ancient city of Babylon was located approximately 100 miles south of present-day Baghdad. Here Babylonians built the Tower of Babel in an attempt to reach heaven. When God disapproved, He prevented the people from communicating with each other by making them speak in different languages. This is where the word "babble" derives its meaning (think about it) and where foreign languages originated. The "Hanging Gardens of Babylon," which was one of the Seven Wonders of the Ancient World, were also created here.

Other worthy inventions that originated in Mesopotamia include the first stringed harp, the sickle for harvesting grain, the first windmills used to pump water and the first soap.

Some of the modern laws used in nearly every form of government today that relate to marriage and divorce, theft, debt and land rights are derived from the legal codes of Babylon. One of the most well-known codes was the Hammurabi Code, which contained laws such as "an eye for an eye, a tooth for a tooth," as well as the practice of cutting off a man's hand for certain crimes.

Speaking of crimes, one modern-day scribe suggested that Iraq should be re-named Mesopotamia once again. Since there's no chance that Saddam will ever return to rule the country, losing the name Iraq might be a good way to give the country and its people a fresh start.

How many of these little-known clues about inventors can you solve?

Choose the correct answers from the following names. Each name is used only once.

Ruth Handler
Philo Farnsworth
David Mulligan
Alfred Nobel
Thomas Jefferson
James Naismith
Samuel Morse
Frank Zamboni
André Marie Ampère
Cyrus McCormick

Zeppo Marx
George Washington Carver
Chester Carlson
Nelson Doubleday
Clarence Birdseye
Thomas Edison
Walt Disney
Charles Goodyear
William Lear
Dr. Pemberton

1. This Frenchman was one of the founders of the theory of electricity.

2. He was a college dropout who conceived of his invention while working in the Arctic.

3. He published a chemical magazine to support his invalid parents when he was in high school, and went on to license his photocopying technology to Xerox.

4. Born to slaves in Missouri and kidnapped by Confederates, he was known as "The Plant Doctor" and later became head of the Department of Agricultural Research at the Tuskegee Institute.

5. His mouse is more than 70 years old.

6. He sometimes gets credit for inventing the game of baseball, and he fired the first shot in defense during the Civil War.

7. His partial deafness helped him concentrate better by being able to block out noise, leading to an invention that helped brighten people's lives.

8. He conceived the idea of television at age 14.

9. This inventor named his heating process after Vulcan, the Roman god of fire, and was $200,000 in debt when he died.

10. She co-founded Mattel before designing a doll which she named after her daughter.

11. Prior to becoming our nation's first patent commissioner, he opposed the concept of granting patents because he considered them to be an unfair monopoly.

12. He established a company to make corporate jets, was a co-inventor of the world's first car radio and was sole inventor of the 8-track tape player. He was also born in the same home town as Mark Twain.

13. One of four famous brothers, he invented a clamping device which was used to strap down the atomic bombs before they were dropped in World War II.

14. The original version of his machine, which led him to start what later became the International Harvester Company, was pulled by horses.

15. Before he became known for the biblical phrase, "What hath God wrought?" he was well-known for his paintings and was commissioned to paint President James Monroe, Eli Whitney and his neighbor Noah Webster.

16. This Canadian golfer invented the do-over in his sport.

17. This Canadian minister created basketball at a YMCA; his rules originally called for each team to have nine players, including a goal keeper (yes, a goal keeper).

18. This "man of peace" invented dynamite.

19. He used coca leaves and the cola nut in his recipe for Coca-Cola.

20. His "cool" invention was first used in southern California long before the NHL had a hockey team there.

ANSWERS:

1. Ampère
2. Birdseye
3. Carlson
4. Carver
5. Disney
6. Doubleday
7. Edison
8. Farnsworth
9. Goodyear
10. Handler
11. Jefferson
12. Lear
13. Marx
14. McCormick
15. Morse
16. Mulligan
17. Naismith
18. Nobel
19. Pemberton
20. Zamboni

You may have noticed a trend developing. The answers to each clue are listed in alphabetical order, according to each inventor's last name.

The year in review looks back at the 5 hottest inventions of '03

Since many inventions take several years or even decades to gain widespread acceptance, let's take a look back at the greatest inventions of '03 ... as in 1903. Since you probably weren't around then, here's a list of the hottest new inventions that were making the news that year — and are now more popular than ever, more than 100 years after they were invented:

- The first motorized, manned airplane
- The electrocardiogram (EKG)
- Crayola® crayons
- The windshield wiper
- The disposable safety razor

There are a number of ways to measure the success of a new invention. For example, how long did it take for the invention to be accepted by society as a whole? How has it improved people's lives? How many people use it? Will it be around in 100 years?

The first motorized, manned airplane

The many news and history stories tell us all we need to know about the Wright Brothers' first flight at Kitty Hawk, but there are a couple of interesting facts about aviation that many people don't know. For example, most of the large airlines today are not profitable, with the exception of Southwest Airlines. It is also statistically safer to fly in an airplane than to ride in a car.

The electrocardiogram (EKG)

Back in 1860, physiologist Willem Einthoven was born in Java of the Dutch East Indies, known today as Indonesia. In 1903, he invented the string galvanometer, which led him to develop the electrocardiogram (EKG), for which he received the 1924 Nobel

Prize. The EKG is a graphic record of the heart's action which tells whether or not the heart is performing normally. Scientists from all over the world would visit Einthoven's laboratory to see his string galvanometer, and today EKG's are used in many developed countries to diagnose heart conditions.

Crayola® crayons

The next product hasn't saved any lives (at least not that we know of), but can you imagine growing up without your Crayola® crayons? Binney & Smith is the company behind Crayolas. Actually, it was Binney's wife, Alice, who came up with the idea as an alternative to the crayons that were being imported from Europe at the time. She also created the Crayola brand name by combining the French words "craie," which meant colored stick and "ola," meaning oily.

The first box of Crayolas sold for a nickel and contained eight crayons – red, orange, yellow, green, blue, violet, brown and black. Today – 100 billion crayons later – the Crayola brand is synonymous with the product.

The windshield wiper

Mary Anderson came up with her idea for a windshield wiper while she was touring New York City on a streetcar in 1903. Watching the motorman constantly get out to wipe the snow and ice from the windshield, she figured there must be a better way, and the rest is history. It took only 10 years for the windshield wiper to become standard equipment on automobiles, yet Mary never pocketed a dime from her invention.

The disposable safety razor

King Camp Gillette invented the first disposable safety razor in 1903. By 1905, he had sold only 168 blades, but sales had jumped to more than 12 million blades the following year. Less than a hundred years later, the company's numerous product lines account for nearly $10 billion in annual sales worldwide.

We'll review the hottest inventions of '04 in the next book in the *Invention Mysteries* series … although the '04 may refer to 1904 or even 1804, which was the year of the first steam locomotive (invented in England), the Jacquard Loom (invented in France) and the Congreve rocket (also invented in England), which 7 years later produced "the rocket's red glare" that Francis Scott Key wrote about in *The Star-Spangled Banner.*

Charles never received much recognition for his life-saving invention

This is the story of an inventor whose work with a first-class doctor led to thousands of lives being saved, yet he didn't receive the recognition that he deserved.

His name was Charles, but I don't want you to feel sorry for him, because Charles didn't want the attention that comes with helping to create a life-saving invention. Charles had earned enough praise for his work in another field, totally unrelated to his work as a medical researcher and inventor.

Besides, since he was already known as the greatest in his field, he would probably not have been taken seriously as a medical researcher. Does anyone remember that Babe Ruth the actor once starred in a movie? Or that Mark Twain the inventor once earned more money from one of his inventions than from his writings that year?

Any unnecessary attention might hinder Charles's work. His motivation came from the fact that his sister-in-law had a serious illness and there wasn't any kind of medical device available that could save her life.

Charles approached Dr. Alexis Carrel of the Rockefeller Institute about working together. An odd pairing, the two hit it off immediately. Carrel, who had won a Nobel Prize for his work on organ transplants, was known as "the father of vascular surgery" and was somewhat quirky. Charles was an amateur medical researcher with nationwide name recognition who chose to work in anonymity.

Dr. Carrel was from France, a country which gave Charles a hero's welcome. He later won a Pulitzer Prize in 1939 for a book that he co-wrote with Charles called *The Culture of Organs*. Charles would later win a Pulitzer Prize of his own for a book in a totally different field.

The two of them went about trying to create a way to keep the heart and other organs alive outside of the body during surgery. The result was a perfusion pump which consisted of an organ chamber, an equalization chamber and a pressure chamber, all contained in a glass container. It was designed to circulate blood through the body during surgery.

Charles created a system of floating valves, using airplane glue to seal the device shut. It had to be a closed system in order to keep things sterile. Charles had even suggested to Carrel that he bypass the heart during cardiac surgery, but Carrel refused. It took another 20 years before another surgeon accomplished open heart surgery in 1954.

When World War II began, both men walked away from their research. Carrel died during the war, ironically, of heart failure while Charles was stationed in the Pacific.

Success and inventing seemed to run in Charles's family. His father was elected to the U.S. Congress five times and later made a run for the Senate, which he lost. His maternal grandfather was the dentist who invented the porcelain crown.

The family of Charles's wife, Anne, was just as successful as Charles's family. Anne's father was a partner of J.P. Morgan as well as an ambassador to Mexico and later a U.S. senator. In fact, it was Anne's anesthesiologist who led Charles to Dr. Carrel. Both Charles and Anne received numerous awards during their life together, yet they were haunted by the death of their infant son early in their marriage.

By now, you've probably figured out who Charles is. If not, here's a re-cap of the clues:

🔆 France, a country which gave Charles a hero's welcome.

🔆 Charles had won a Pulitzer Prize for his book.

🔆 Charles used airplane glue to seal the system of floating valves shut.

🔆 Charles and Anne were haunted by the death of their infant son.

The book was *The Spirit of St. Louis*, which Charles Lindbergh wrote in 1953.

Since Charles's second career would probably have been overshadowed by his first – as was the case with actor Babe Ruth and inventor Mark Twain – he probably would not have been taken seriously as a medical researcher and inventor.

The invention came to be known as the Carrel-Lindbergh perfusion pump. Lindbergh's contribution was the perfusion system and the centrifuge which he made to separate blood plasma without damaging it. Charles didn't really create the first artificial heart as has been reported, but rather a way to keep organs alive outside the body during surgery.

Did bootleggers help invent NASCAR?

"Bootleggers, start your engines!"

In a story that you won't find on the official NASCAR web site, stock car racing got its start with bootleggers running moonshine whiskey in the 1920's and early 30's. During Prohibition in the South, bootleggers would haul their moonshine from their home-made stills to customers at night with the cars' lights turned off to avoid detection by the law. To avoid being stopped when the police spotted them, the bootleggers modified their cars so they could outrun the police.

Eventually the bootleggers wanted something more challenging than outrunning the law, so they began racing each other with the souped-up engines. They would haul moonshine Sunday night in the same cars they raced on Sunday afternoons. A new sport was born.

After Prohibition ended in 1933, the government placed heavy taxes on liquor sales, so bootlegging showed no signs of ending. The fact that there are dry counties in the South reminds me of the summer I spent in Florence, Alabama, in 1987. On the way to work each morning, I drove past a liquor store near the county line where the sign out front revealed the store's name as "Last Chance Liquors" because it was the last chance to buy alcohol before entering a dry county. Driving back into the wet county each night, I'd notice that the other side of the sign referred to that same liquor store as "First Chance Liquors."

"Gentlemen, start your engines!"

There are probably some NASCAR fans who think that these words are the last four words of the national anthem. NASCAR, which stands for National Association for Stock Car Auto Racing, has become the fastest growing spectator sport in the country. Its modern roots go all the way back to 1938 when Bill France, Sr.

organized a race at Daytona Beach, Florida. France was one of NASCAR's first racers before it became NASCAR, and some of the sport's earliest racers were veterans of the bootlegging circuit.

The sport grew in popularity, but racing came to a screeching halt during World War II. After the war, in 1947, Bill France realized that the sport needed some organization to it, with its own set of rules, regulations and records. He brought promoters to Daytona Beach to organize the governing body of auto racing. NASCAR had begun.

The first NASCAR race was held in Charlotte, N.C. in June of 1949. The winner of that race was Glenn Dunnaway in a '47 Ford. Dunnaway was disqualified, though, when inspectors found an illegal part in his car's shock absorbers. The illegal part was often used to make bootlegging cars go faster, and the car had been used for bootlegging earlier that week.

Auto racing led to the development of an important invention that we all use everyday – the rearview mirror. In the early days of racing, racers had a passenger riding shotgun to let them know where the other cars were behind them. The added weight slowed the cars down a bit, but the rearview mirror solved this problem.

In a bit of irony to this story, NASCAR, the sport whose earliest participants got their start running moonshine whiskey, does not allow liquor companies to advertise hard liquor on the race cars or to sponsor NASCAR races.

This inventor didn't regret missing out on an $8 million fortune

Sometimes two people cross paths and it changes history. Sometimes a business deal works out well for one person but not the other.

Joshua L. Cowen's family arrived in New York shortly after the Civil War.

Conrad Hubert immigrated to America in 1890 to avoid being persecuted as a Jew in his native Russia.

In 1898, the two met and became friends. Joshua was an inventor running a business. Conrad was particularly interested in one of Joshua's inventions, an "electric flowerpot," so Joshua let his friend have it for practically free. Joshua was more interested in inventing than in running a business anyway.

Conrad re-designed the electric flowerpot by placing the battery and bulb inside a tube, and called it an "electric hand torch." Field and Stream magazine later re-named it as the flashlight.

While Conrad went on to amass an $8 million fortune, 22-year old Joshua founded another company in 1900 in a small, third-floor loft in Manhattan. He didn't mind that he had sold his electric flowerpot for so little, as he was now doing what he really enjoyed – inventing.

By 1953, Joshua's company had become the largest toymaker in the world, although it has since declined. Joshua had named the company after himself, but that doesn't tell you much because he named it after his middle name.

He wasn't the first to invent this type of product, but he was the first to use electricity to run it, as electricity was still rare in American homes in the early 1900's. The product, whose origin probably began when Joshua whittled a miniature wooden model of it at age seven, was originally designed as a window display for stores. When Joshua noticed that people wanted to buy the display item, he decided to make them available for sale.

You might not recognize the name of Joshua Lionel Cowen, even though his invention has bonded fathers and sons for more than 100 years, but I know you've heard of the Lionel Manufacturing Company, which has sold more than 50 million trains since it began more than a century ago.

So the story about a man who basically gave away a product that led to another man's fortune has a happy ending of its own.

Lionel's earliest trains were powered by batteries. Who did he buy his batteries from?

I don't know the answer to that one, but I'd like to think that he bought them from the company run by his friend, Conrad Hubert. The name of that company?

Eveready Battery.

Today, Eveready/Energizer is the world's largest manufacturer of batteries and flashlights, and is headquartered in St. Louis, Missouri with more than 10,000 employees in 140 countries.

Kind of interesting how these things work out, isn't it?

A brief history of milestone patents, copyrights and trademarks

This story traces the history of intellectual property in America. Patents, trademarks and copyrights aren't an American invention, though, as they originated in Europe.

The first patent ever issued went to architect Filippo Brunelleschi of Florence, Italy, for his method of transporting goods up the Arno River in 1421. The patent was for a 3-year period.

American patents were originally issued by individual states. The first state patent issued went to Samuel Winslow of Massachusetts in 1641 for his new method of making salt. After Congress enacted federal patent laws in 1790, President George Washington personally signed each patent, as was customary at the time. Secretary of State Thomas Jefferson, an avid inventor himself, became the first patent commissioner that same year, even though he originally opposed patents because he considered them to be an unfair monopoly.

The first federal U.S. patent was issued to Samuel Hopkins of Vermont for his method of making potash. The fee to obtain the patent? A whopping four dollars! Today, patent fees average $4,000.

Prior to being issued patent numbers, patents contained the inventor's name and date of the patent. There were already 10,000 patents issued without numbers when the Patent Office started issuing numbers in July of 1836. A Mr. John Ruggles received U.S. Patent # 1 for his "traction wheels."

The one-millionth patent was issued in 1911 to Francis Holton for his new type of vehicle tire. It took 75 years to get to Patent #1,000,000, yet it took only eight years to go from Patent #5,000,000 in 1991 (a method of producing ethanol by E-coli strains), to Patent #6,000,000 in 1999 (a method of sharing files among computers).

Mary Kies is believed to be the first woman to receive a patent, for her process of weaving straw with silk in 1809. I use the word "believed" because women were not allowed to own property during parts of the 1700's and 1800's. As a result, there may have been other women who received patents by using only their initials prior to Mary Kies, while other women simply filed for patents in their husbands' names.

There were times in the 1800's when slaves were not allowed to own property, and this included intellectual property such as patents, trademarks and copyrights. Thomas Jennings was a free man running a dry cleaning business in New York City in 1821 when he became the first black man to receive a patent (for a dry cleaning process). He used some of his earnings from that patent to buy his family out of slavery.

Surprisingly, an 1861 law passed by the pro-slavery Confederate States of America granted patent rights to slaves. Nine years later, the U.S. government passed a law that gave all black men patent rights.

Sarah Goode owned a furniture store in Chicago when she patented a cabinet bed in 1885, becoming the first black woman to receive a U.S. patent.

The federal patent laws that Congress enacted in 1790 also governed trademarks and copyrights. A trademark is a word or symbol that identifies the source of a product or company. The world's first trademark is believed to be for two British chefs named Crosse & Blackwell in 1706. It is still in use today – the trademark, that is, not the chefs!

Some of the more memorable American trademarks have been based on people, such as the leprechaun symbolizing Notre Dame's Fighting Irish, the Gerber baby and the Morton Salt girl. Other trademarks have been based on animals such as the MGM lion, Smokey Bear and Borden's top sales lady, Elsie the Cow. Trademarks don't need to be based on a real person or animal to be effective, as Planters' Mr. Peanut, Prudential's Rock of Gibraltar and the Pillsbury Doughboy have all become permanently etched into our memories.

A copyright protects literary works such as books, plays, articles, poems, songs, movies, pictures and paintings. A copyright lasts for the life of the author plus 70 years.

Even a U.S. president can receive a patent, a trademark or a copyright. George Washington received a trademark for his brand of flour in 1772, and Abraham Lincoln received a patent in 1849 for a device to help boats navigate in shallow waters. Thomas Jefferson, the nation's most successful presidential inventor, chose not to patent any of his inventions.

So how does one know whether a product has been patented, trademarked, or copyrighted?

A patented product contains the patent number on the packaging; a trademarked product is shown with the TM symbol (™) or an "R" inside a circle (®), if it's a registered trademark. A copyrighted material contains a "C" inside a circle (©), along with the year and name of the copyright owner.

Celebrate Black History Month
with these inventors

February is known as Black History Month, so we celebrate some of the top African-American inventors whose contributions have played a significant role in benefiting society. As with any kind of story about the biggest, brightest or best, there's not enough room to mention them all, so we'll take a look at several black inventors who I think are particularly interesting.

The most prolific African-American inventor of all time is agricultural chemist George Washington Carver. Born to slave parents on a farm near Joplin, Missouri, in 1860, George spent much of his early years exploring the wooded areas on the family farm, becoming known as the "Plant Doctor" in his community.

George invented more than 300 uses for peanuts and hundreds of additional uses for other plants. Some of the products resulting from Carver's work include: adhesives, axle grease, bleach, buttermilk, chili sauce, ink, instant coffee, linoleum, mayonnaise, meat tenderizer, metal polish, paper, plastic, pavement, shaving cream, shoe polish, synthetic rubber and talcum powder. Carver later became director of the Department of Agricultural Research at Tuskegee Institute (in Tuskegee, Alabama) when he was just 36 years old.

Sounds like George Washington Carver was the real McCoy among inventors, right?

No, that would be Elijah McCoy, a Canadian inventor born in 1844 to former slaves. McCoy's automatic oiling cup for trains became known as "The Real McCoy" when engineers began asking for it by name.

Staying on the subject of trains, Granville T. Woods (1856 - 1910) invented a telegraph that allowed moving trains to communicate with other trains and with train stations. This improved railway efficiency and safety and also made it harder for bandits to rob trains. In addition to having a really cool first name, Woods was nicknamed "The Black Edison." He was awarded more than 60 patents during his lifetime.

There was probably no inventor who surrounded himself with better company than Lewis Latimer (1848 - 1929). He was the only inventor who worked with both Alexander Graham Bell and Thomas Edison. First he helped Bell draft his blueprints for the telephone, then he and a co-worker created the carbon filament for Edison's electric light bulb. This replaced Edison's bamboo filament that lasted only 30 hours and shattered when it got too hot. Latimer and his co-worker also created a process for making the carbon filaments.

The parents of some of America's greatest black inventors were slaves and, even though the Civil War had ended, slavery had left many of them poor. Blacks were not welcome in many parts of America, and the fact that they had little, if any, schooling makes their achievements even more incredible.

The gas mask that Garrett Morgan invented saved the lives of thousands of soldiers in World War I. Morgan (1875 - 1963) even used one of his gas masks to help rescue men trapped by a gas explosion in a tunnel being built under Lake Erie. Morgan also invented the automatic traffic signal.

The first black woman inventor to achieve millionaire status was Sarah Breedlove Walker, a.k.a. Madame C.J. Walker (1867 - 1919). Perhaps no one faced harsher obstacles than Madame Walker. A widow at age 20, she faced racial discrimination as well as sex discrimination.

Madame Walker created a new hair process with the aid of the straightening comb that she invented and patented in 1905. She developed a line of cosmetics for black women that led to a business empire that employed more than 3,000 people. She later shared her wealth with many black charities.

So who invented Black History Month? And why was February chosen as the month to celebrate it?

Dr. Carter Woodson led a group of black and white scholars in establishing "Negro History Week" in Chicago in 1926. Dr. Woodson chose a week in February because it's the month in which two people who had a huge impact on the lives of black

Americans were born – Abraham Lincoln and abolitionist Frederick Douglass.

Like many of the inventors profiled in this story, Woodson was the son of former slaves and was born into poverty. The group that he founded, the Association for the Study of African American Life and History, expanded Negro History Week into Black History Month in 1976 as part of the nation's bicentennial celebration.

What does "QWERTY" have to do with Valentine's Day?

Before we jump into the usual topic of inventions, let's start with a brief history of Valentine's Day. There were actually three different men named Valentine, and all three became martyrs.

Around 270 A.D., the emperor Claudius banned marriage in the Roman empire. His reasoning was that married men were weak soldiers. A Catholic priest named Valentine secretly married the couples that came to him. When Claudius found out, Valentine tried to convert him. He failed, though, and the emperor had him imprisoned before executing him. While he was in prison, he fell in love with the jailer's blind daughter and cured her. Upon Valentine's departure, he gave her a farewell message that read, "From your Valentine."

Legend has it that the middle of February may have been chosen as Valentine's Day because it was the mating season of birds during the Middle Ages in Europe. I guess that clears up the misconception that Hallmark created the holiday. Actually, Valentine's Day was created in the 5th century A.D. to replace a pagan festival. As for Cupid, he was the son of Venus, the Roman god of love.

Now back to our story.

Two of the most notable Valentine's Day inventions came from Christopher Sholes and George Ferris. Since you know what Ferris invented, we'll start with Sholes.

As you type away on your computer keyboard, have you ever wondered why the letters are arranged that way? Why didn't they just put them in alphabetical order?

Christopher Sholes was born on Valentine's Day in 1819 in Danville, Pennsylvania. He was a two-time Wisconsin state senator who helped found the Wisconsin Republican Party before he invented the first practical typewriter in 1872.

In the early days of typewriters, people used the two-finger "hunt and peck" method that's still popular today. The letters of Sholes' typewriter were originally arranged in alphabetical order, and a typewriter tended to jam when the user typed too fast. To solve this problem, Sholes re-designed the keyboard so that the most common letters were farther away from each other, hoping to slow down the rate of typing and reduce the jamming. The result is the QWERTY design which you see on every typewriter and computer keyboard (look at the top row of letters to figure out why it was named QWERTY).

The following year, Sholes sold the rights of his typewriter to Remington, which is the same company that makes Remington rifles. He later added the shift key so that people could type lowercase letters as well as uppercase letters.

Mark Twain, who sometimes invested in new inventions, was the first author to submit a typewritten manuscript to his publisher.

As for George Ferris and his wheel, George Washington Gale Ferris was born on Valentine's Day in 1859 in Galesburg, Illinois, and moved with his family to Carson City, Nevada, at age five. There was a second person named George Ferris who was born just two weeks after the first one. He also moved to Carson City, but it was much later than when the first George Ferris lived there.

Like Sholes, Ferris was also an engineer. George built the Ferris wheel for sight-seeing purposes, and it made its debut at the Chicago Fair in 1893. It was 264 feet tall and had 36 cars, each one seating 40 people. It carried more than one million paying customers during the nineteen weeks of the fair, grossing a little more than $725,000 (that's more than $15.5 million in today's money).

A duplicate of the wheel was constructed for the 1900 Paris Exposition, while the original wheel was taken down and re-constructed in St. Louis for the 1904 Exposition. Two years later, it was torn down.

Ferris' wife stopped the wheel when it reached the top for the very first time and toasted him. What a great way to celebrate Valentine's Day! What a great way to end this story!

Actually, it didn't happen on Valentine's Day. It happened in June. And this story is not quite over yet.

A few other interesting events surround Valentine's Day. Two states, Oregon and Arizona, were added to the union on Valentine's day. Oregon became the 33rd state in 1859 and Arizona became the 48th state in 1912. Two other well-known people were born on Valentine's Day – Jimmy Hoffa in 1913 and Mrs. Brady herself, Florence Henderson, in 1934.

Now the story is officially over.

Would the inventors of ice skates
have believed in miracles?

In 1980 in Lake Placid, New York, the American hockey team shocked the world. First we defeated the Soviet Union in the early medal round, and then we beat Finland to bring home the Gold medal. It was the first time an American hockey team ever won Gold, and many of us remember announcer Al Michaels proclaiming, "Do you believe in miracles? Yes!"

The recent movie about that 1980 Olympic team made me wonder how some hockey-related inventions were created. Let's take a look at three of them.

Ice Skates

You'd probably think that ice skates were invented by a Canadian. After all, that's where hockey originated, right? And hockey is the national sport of Canada, eh?

I grew up playing "pond hockey" on our farm — we even used our Jeep to plow the snow off the pond one time — and then went on to play hockey at the University of Kentucky. Many people think hockey in Kentucky makes about as much sense as a Jamaican bobsled team.

The Dutch word for skate is "schenkel" which means "leg bone." A pair of primitive skates found at the bottom of a lake in Switzerland date back to around 3,000 B.C. Believe it or not, these skates were made from the leg bones of large animals, with holes bored at each end of the bones. Leather straps were used to tie on the skates.

During the 1300's, the Dutch developed skates that were attached to the skater's shoes with leather straps, and they used poles to propel themselves forward. Around 1500, they added a metal double-edged blade, which made the poles unnecessary because the skater could now push and glide with his feet.

There have been a number of innovations added to ice skates since then, such as attaching the blade directly to the boots and adding toe picks (known as teeth). While figure skates allow a skater to make the jumps that you see in competitions on TV, the toothless hockey skates allow a skater to change direction easier and to stop quicker.

Hockey may or may not have originated in Canada. Just as in baseball, there are different versions of how and where the game originated. Some believe that hockey's roots go all the way back to the 16th century in Europe, with the word hockey being derived from the French word "hoquet," which means "bent stick."

North American hockey originated in Canada, and it may have evolved from a game called "Ice Hurley" in the early 1800's in Nova Scotia. The first official hockey game was played in 1886 on a Canadian rink that had a grandstand in the middle of the ice. The "puck" was actually a lacrosse ball cut into the shape of a square. After that came wooden pucks; today the pucks are made of hard rubber.

Inline Skates

Like ice skates, inline skates also have a Dutch origin that goes back several centuries. In the 1700's, a Dutchman tried to simulate ice skating by nailing wooden spools to strips of wood that he attached to the bottoms of his shoes.

In 1980, an NHL player named Scott Olson bought an old pair of inline skates at a sporting goods store in Minnesota because he thought they would be a good training device for hockey during the off-season. (No, they weren't the Dutch skates left over from the 1700's.)

Olson named his inline skates Rollerblades and later sold the rights to an established company. The skates became a hot-selling item after they were introduced in Southern California.

Zamboni Machine

Just as Rollerblades made their mark in Southern California, so did the company that Frank Zamboni founded to build the machines that bear his name. Zamboni Machines® cover the rink with a brand new layer of ice between each period of hockey games and during figure skating competitions.

Since the Zamboni factory is located about a mile down the street from the ice rink where they test them, local residents sometimes get to watch a Zamboni employee drive one of these machines on the road. They have a top speed of nine miles per hour.

By the way, hockey is not the national sport of Canada. Lacrosse is. And in case you haven't heard, there really is a Jamaican bobsled team. They placed 14th at the 1994 Olympics, ahead of the U.S. and Russian teams.

Could Thomas Edison be considered a failure?

The greatest inventor in American history also had the most failures. This reminds me of the fact that Babe Ruth, the man who held the records for most home runs in a season and in a career, also held the record for the most strikeouts.

Even a young Elvis Presley appeared to have some shortcomings. After a performance early in his career at the Grand Ole Opry, someone told the King, "You ain't goin' nowhere, son."

Thomas Edison, the man who invented the incandescent light bulb, as well as the phonograph, the motion picture camera, a stock ticker, a vote recorder and the electric motor, had many failures.

Edison tried – and failed – to use cement to build small things such as cabinets and pianos. Concrete was just too expensive at the time.

He was also one of many inventors who tried – and failed – to combine sound and motion to make talking movies. Actually, he was in good company because nearly everyone else who tried doing that also failed, and there were quite a few who tried.

One of Edison's greatest failures was being unable to create a practical way to mine iron ore. He lost every penny that he invested in the project.

His electric vote recorder, which worked but was a commercial failure, taught him a valuable business lesson. It led him to conclude, "I only want to invent things that will sell."

Oh, and that light bulb only came about after he endured 10,000 failed attempts.

How did all of the failures affect Edison?

Apparently, it made him stronger. He once remarked that he hadn't failed 10,000 times, but rather that he discovered 10,000 ways that would not work! Talk about making lemonade when handed a bunch of lemons. He saw that each failed attempt brought him a little closer to the solution he was searching for.

In fact, Edison wasn't even the first inventor to invent a light bulb when he perfected his incandescent bulb in 1878. A British inventor named Joseph Swan had developed a different version a year earlier. But Edison established the framework to light entire cities.

Despite the title of this story, I'm not trying to convince you that Edison was a failure. You see, the man who is regarded as the most successful inventor in American history is the same man who had the most failures as an inventor. Like Babe Ruth and Elvis Presley, Edison didn't let his failures slow him down.

His reputation as the greatest inventor of all time comes not just from having the most patents (he received 1,093 patents) but also for having the most impact on society with his inventions. Just about every person living in a civilized society has benefited from at least one of his inventions. This is even more impressive when you consider that Edison was nearly deaf and that his formal schooling didn't go beyond the third grade. One of young Thomas Edison's teachers even remarked that he was "too stupid to learn."

Where Edison failed on a small scale, he was usually able to succeed on a larger scale. Most successful inventors create new products, but Edison created an entire industry – the electric industry. His light bulb, along with the power grid that he built to allow his light bulbs to keep entire cities bright at night, led to the creation of what is known today as General Electric.

And while Edison failed on a small scale with making certain products out of cement, he succeeded on a very large scale with cement. It was his company, the Edison Portland Cement Company, which built Yankee Stadium ... forever known as "The House That Ruth Built."

Where did the Barbie Doll and Baby Ruth originate?

This story features two success stories and the real-life women behind them. One was born to a very successful female CEO at a time when there weren't many women executives in corporate America, while the other was supposedly born to a First Lady.

One has its roots in the proverbial "inventor's garage," while the other was supposedly born in the White House.

One woman was one of the first female CEO's in our country's history, while the other was supposedly the first child born to a president's family in the White House. The first story is based on indisputable truth, while the second one is either truth or urban legend, depending on who you want to believe. I'm talking, both figuratively and literally, about the Barbie Doll and the Baby Ruth candy bar.

Barbie Doll:

Prior to the three-dimensional Barbie Doll, most dolls were two-dimensional and made of cardboard. They came with paper dresses with little tabs that bent over the edges of the doll, as well as hats with slits to slide over their heads. Like her cardboard predecessor, the Barbie Dolls were also patterned after full-grown women. Ruth Handler wanted to create a doll that inspired girls to think about what they wanted to become when they got older.

Ruth named the Barbie Doll after her daughter. She also created the Mattel name in 1943 when she combined the names of the company's co-founders, her husband Elliot Handler and Harold Mattson. Barbie has accompanied millions of girls through their childhood years. Barbie's boyfriend Ken was named after the real-life Barbie's real-life brother. More than a billion Barbie Dolls have been sold since Barbie arrived on the scene at the annual Toy Fair in New York City in 1959. Oddly enough, when Handler approached the all-male group of ad executives at Mattel, the group rejected her Barbie Doll idea because they thought the doll was too expensive and didn't have enough potential.

The Barbie Doll is the toy industry's most successful product line of all time, a line that consists of more than 600 different Barbies. A Barbie was even included in the official "America's Time Capsule" buried at the 1976 Bicentennial celebration. The Handlers left the company in the mid-1970's.

Baby Ruth:

The Baby Ruth candy bar made its debut in 1921, a product of the Curtiss Candy Company. The company claims that the bar was named after President Grover Cleveland's baby daughter, who was born in 1892, not the baseball player Babe Ruth.

This is where it gets interesting – and where urban legend comes into play.

The Curtiss Candy Company claims that the name and the style of lettering for the candy bar was patterned after a medallion at a Chicago expo in 1893 which pictured the former president, along with his wife and daughter.

Curtiss Candy Company's main office was in Chicago, and their official explanation of the bar's name was, "Our candy bar made its initial appearance in 1921, some years before Babe Ruth ... became famous. The similarity of names, therefore, is purely coincidental." The company went on to explain that Ruth Cleveland (President Cleveland's daughter) visited the Curtiss Candy Company when the company was just getting started. Since Ruth Cleveland had died at the age of 12 in 1904 and the company wasn't founded until 1916, I'm going to go out on a limb and say that their claim wasn't totally accurate. Then again, the company was located in Chicago and the expo where the presidential medallion was displayed was also in Chicago. Plus, the candy bar was named "Baby Ruth" rather than "Babe Ruth."

By 1921, Babe Ruth had become a famous Yankees outfielder, while Grover Cleveland had been out of office for more than 25 years (and his daughter had been dead for almost 17 years). This makes it hard to believe that the candy bar was named after Ruth Cleveland.

So are we really supposed to believe that the company named the candy bar after the former president's daughter rather than a rising star like Babe Ruth? It's hard to say for sure. Some things are better left to the imagination, so we'll let you decide for yourself.

Here's a brief history lesson on some favorite trademarks

Most of the stories in this book reveal a few of the little-known stories behind well-known inventions. This story examines a few well-known trademarks.

A trademark identifies the brand name of a product or company. It is initially shown with a small ™ symbol, and is later shown with an "R" inside of a circle (®) once it's been registered with the U.S. Patent & Trademark Office.

Have a Coke and a smile:

The most famous trademark in the world belongs to Coca-Cola. Atlanta pharmacist and Civil War veteran John Pinkerton invented the soft drink in 1886, but his friend and bookkeeper, F.M. Robinson, gave the drink its name.

Most people know that Coca-Cola originally contained cocaine extracts as well as caffeine from the kola nut, hence the name.

While Coke made a big mistake by introducing New Coke in 1985, they made an even bigger mistake when they decided to turn down an opportunity to purchase the Pepsi brand in the early 1900's. You can't really blame Coke, though, because there were a number of small cola companies back then, and there was no way to know that Pepsi would someday become its biggest competitor.

Get your kicks on Route 66:

The employees of most companies can tell you the story of how their company got its name. Many of the employees of Phillips 66 cannot. The story behind the Phillips 66 name has many possible explanations – and none of them have any basis in truth.

According to the book *Famous American Trademarks*, these explanations include:

☀ "Frank Phillips was 66 years old when he started the company." He was actually 44 at the time.

☀ "The 66 referred to the octane level of the gasoline." The truth is that octane ratings weren't adopted until five years after the company began.

☀ "The 66 was based on the 'fact' that there are 66 books in the Bible." Again, not true, but thanks for playing.

☀ "The company basketball team won by 66 points the night before the name was chosen." The actual margin of victory was 18 points.

☀ "The first Phillips station sold 6,600 gallons of gas the first day." Nice try, but it sold 12,000 gallons. Besides, wouldn't the company have decided on a name before it opened for business?

So how did the company get its name?

The idea to use 66 in the name had been suggested earlier, but it was rejected. It made sense, given the company's close proximity to Route 66 and the fact that their "fuel gravity" was close to 66.

Eventually, a Phillips employee was testing the new fuel when he remarked, "This car goes like 60 (miles per hour)."

The driver replied, "Sixty, nothing. We're doing 66."

Where did this happen?

On Route 66, near Tulsa. Of course!

Overnight success:

Federal Express founder Fred Smith was a Yale student in 1965 when he submitted a term paper for his economics class detailing his idea of an overnight delivery service. He was a member of the highly secret and highly selective "Skull & Bones" Club, the same club that President George W. Bush belonged to during his days at Yale.

FedEx, the company that was founded with a record amount of venture capital financing (at the time) and now produces more than $20 billion in annual sales, is the premier next-day package delivery company in the world. Like Coca-Cola, its trademark is so well-known that it has become a generic brand name.

As for its founder, Fred Smith, what grade did he receive on that term paper?

He got a "C."

So even if your favorite brands include such little-known secrets as having cocaine extract in its original formula or having the origin of the company name remain unknown by its employees, or if its business plan received a grade of "C," the brand could still do just fine.

Who invented the modern baseball glove?

As you enter the main office of Rawlings Sporting Goods near St. Louis, you can't help but notice the wall decorations.

This is no ordinary office because it's the headquarters of the exclusive supplier of Major League baseballs. The company also supplies gloves to more baseball players than any other glove company. In fact, you could say that Rawlings invented the modern baseball glove.

Rawlings was founded in 1887 by two brothers, George and Alfred Rawlings, and their name is still synonymous with baseball nearly 120 years later. We take a look at an invention that's become a part of almost every father and son's life. You could even say that it's one of the most important inventions since medieval times. I may be a bit biased in my judgment of the glove's importance, but if you're a baseball fan, you can probably relate.

What catches your attention as you enter Rawlings' main entrance are the baseball bats hanging from the walls. Each bat has the name of a major league team carved into it, and the bats are placed from top to bottom according to their standings in their respective divisions. They update the team's standings daily. It's like being in baseball heaven.

In the early days of professional baseball, the baseball gloves were not connected between the glove's thumb and index finger. The idea for the webbing between the index finger and thumb on every baseball and softball glove that is in use today came about when a man named Bill Doak stopped by the Rawlings plant one day and suggested a way to improve the glove. At the time, Rawlings was located just a few miles from where the St. Louis Cardinals played their games.

Who was Bill Doak?

"Spittin' Bill" Doak made his major league debut in 1912, a year in which the World Series went eight games because one game ended in a tie. Doak earned his nickname as a spitball-throwing pitcher with the St. Louis Cardinals during a time when spit balls were legal. When Major League Baseball outlawed spitballs in 1920, Bill Doak and the sixteen other spitball pitchers were allowed to continue throwing the spitter under a grandfather clause.

If you can't imagine playing baseball with a glove that doesn't have webbing between the thumb and index finger, then try to imagine what it felt like to play without a glove, because that's how the first professional players did it during much of the 1800's.

For example, when one Cardinals player wore a thin glove for the first time in 1875, he was ridiculed by fans, by opposing players and even by his own teammates! A rule change in the mid-1880's which allowed pitchers to pitch over-handed resulted in line drives coming off the bat much harder than before. As a result, most of the players started wearing gloves.

Have you ever wondered how the glove companies get major league players to endorse their gloves and bats?

They offer "glove contracts" to minor league players before they make it to the major leagues. The players then get free gloves in exchange for the future use of their names on the gloves if and when they make it to the majors.

In an interesting twist to this story, the company that manufactured baseballs for the Major League teams prior to Rawlings was a sporting goods company known as Spalding. That company's founder was a Hall of Fame pitcher for the Chicago White Stockings named Al Spalding, and Al started the debate over who invented baseball more than 50 years earlier — Alexander Cartwright or Abner Doubleday.

For the record, it was Cartwright who invented the rules of modern baseball, while Civil War veteran Doubleday laid out four bases on a diamond and called it baseball in 1839 in Cooperstown, New York, which is where baseball's Hall of Fame is located.

Spalding's company was the official supplier of major league baseballs for 100 years — from 1876 to 1976 — until St. Louis-based Rawlings became the official supplier. Could that have anything to do with the rivalry between the Cardinals and Cubs?

Was an author named Richard
the first person to discover electricity?

Long ago there was a popular author who went by the name of Richard. His best-selling book is still available more than 200 years after his death. Richard was a pretty good inventor, too; in fact, some of his inventions and ideas are still being used today.

Besides being an author, he was also a scientist, a statesman, a printer, an economist, a musician and a philosopher.

Did I mention that he was also the first Postmaster General of the United States? His work as postmaster general inspired him to invent the odometer, which measured the distance that mail carriers traveled. Why was it important to measure the distance they traveled? Because it would be another 80 years before someone would invent postage stamps, and the postage rate was calculated by the distance the mail carrier had to travel to deliver it. Then the recipient of the letter, not the sender, would pay the postage due.

Richard was also the first person to have his image appear on a U.S. stamp. Oddly enough, the second person to have his image appear on a stamp was George Washington.

You say you haven't heard of him?

Maybe it would help if you knew his full name: Richard Saunders. Richard introduced some pretty original sayings in his book, such as "Haste makes waste" and "Early to bed, and early to rise makes a man healthy, wealthy, and wise."

His father had earlier landed in Boston when he immigrated to America looking for religious freedom. Born in 1706, Richard was the youngest of 16 kids – including 6 half siblings born to his father's first wife. Like his father, he was the youngest son of a youngest son; in fact, he was one of five consecutive generations of youngest sons.

A man with many successful inventions and ideas, he was the first to suggest the idea of daylight-saving time. This idea was years ahead of its time, though, as daylight-saving time wasn't implemented until long after Richard died. He had invented many things, but he chose to give them away rather than profit from them.

It was the lightning rod which resulted from his greatest accomplishment.

You still haven't heard of him?

You probably have, but you just don't realize it. Not yet, anyway. Maybe it would help if you knew that he was one of the signers of the Declaration of Independence, even though you won't find Richard Saunders' name anywhere on the document. You've probably heard of his popular book, *Poor Richard's Almanack*, which he published each year for 25 years.

Richard was instrumental in one of the five greatest inventions of all time: the discovery and use of electricity. That was Richard's main claim to fame. You see, he conducted a simple experiment with a kite and a key which enabled him to tap into the power of electricity.

That's impossible, you say – Richard Saunders didn't discover electricity.

Actually, Richard wasn't his real name; it was his pen name. His real name was ... Ben Franklin.

The verdict is in on these ridiculous inventions

It's time for our list of the most ridiculous inventions ever created. If the Patent Office ever decided to create a blooper reel, these inventions would surely make the cut.

These are real inventions which the inventors actually thought would succeed – as opposed to ideas that never made it to the drawing board, such as a submarine with a sunroof, an inflatable dartboard or a helicopter with an ejector seat (think about it).

To get maximum enjoyment out of this story, try to imagine what these inventions would look like. If they were on the market – and trust me, they're not – you could purchase them in order to "Not keep up with the Joneses." Here are the nominees …

10. **The keg head:** This 9-inch mini keg sits on the sports fan's head, and comes complete with a spigot for dispensing any type of drink. It's ideal for the fan who doesn't want to leave his seat for fear of missing a great play.

9. **The toilet tank aquarium:** I love inventions that are so descriptively named, because it's pretty easy to figure out what this one would look like. Have you ever asked yourself, "Now, why didn't I think of that?"

8. **The parachute hat::** This one would work just as you would picture it to work – if only it would work. It was probably intended as a way to escape a burning building … okay, now it makes perfect sense! The parachute hat comes to us from England, and I sure hope they don't have any plans to export it.

7. **A helmet fitted with a rifle:** This is another contraption dreamed up by those clever British. The recoil broke a guinea pig's neck during the experimentation phase. Unfortunately, the guinea pig was a real person.

6. **Eye glasses for chickens:** This one isn't as far-fetched as it sounds, because chickens have been known to peck at each other's eyes.

5. **The process of reincarnation or rebirth which results in immortality:** I wonder if the inventor created this process in this lifetime or in a previous lifetime? It kind of makes you wonder what the inventor did for a living in his previous life.

4. **Training pants for dogs:** We'll leave this one alone.

3. **Tricycle lawnmower:** Some things were just meant to go together ... like a clock and radio, or chocolate and peanut butter, but not tricycles and lawnmowers.

2. **A coffin with an escape hatch:** This would be ideal for the inventor of # 5 above.

And the "winner" is ...

1. **The bird harness:** Like each of the inventions above, this is a true story. It is so bizarre that it would be impossible to make this stuff up. A lady put a bird harness on her bird and took the bird to the park, only to see it get spooked by the sound of flying ducks, who were spooked by a dog. The bird – while attached to the bird harness – flies to a nearby tree and gets stuck. As the poor little bird tries to escape, he accidentally hangs himself.

How is it possible that any of these inventions could receive a patent?

In order to be granted a patent, an invention must meet three criteria: it must be new; it must be "unobvious" to people in that particular industry; and it must be useful. Each of these inventions could be considered new and unobvious, but it's hard to imagine how they can be considered useful.

It's time for a quiz on your favorite inventors and inventions

It's that time again – time to review what we learned in previous stories. As my gift to you the Education Division here at Invention Mysteries World Headquarters provides you with a fun quiz. You can use it to entertain your guests with some fun trivia. Grading is as follows:

A = 13 - 15 correct
B = 10 - 12 correct
C = 7 - 9 correct
D = 4 - 6 correct
F = 0 - 3 correct

Some of the answers can be found in previous stories in this book. All of the answers are found at the end of the quiz.

1. Which Charles invented the "perfusion pump," which paved way for doctors to perform open-heart surgery by providing a way to keep organs alive outside the body during surgery?
    A) Charles Dickens
    B) Charles Lindbergh
    C) Charles Darwin
    D) Charlie Brown

2. Conrad Hubert founded the Eveready Battery Company with a product known as an "electric flowerpot," which he re designed into the world's first flashlight. He bought the rights to the electric flowerpot from his friend, Joshua Lionel Cowen Which company did Cowen start?

3. *TRUE or FALSE?* The fee for the first federal patent issued in the U.S. was only $4. (Today, patent fees average $4,000.)

4. *TRUE or FALSE?* The first patent issued to a woman happened in the 1800's.

5. What was inventor Lewis Latimer's claim to fame? He lived from 1848 - 1929.

6. Inventors Christopher Sholes (who invented the QWERTY keyboard layout) and George Ferris (Ferris Wheel) were born on which holiday?

7. The first known version of this invention – which the Dutch named "schenkel," or "leg bone" – was first found in the bottom of a Swiss lake dating back to around 3,000 B.C. It was made from the leg bones of large animals, with holes bored at eachend of the bones. The modern version is used to play a certain popular winter sport.

8. This inventor, whose first name was Thomas, founded the cement company that built Yankee Stadium. When he was six years old, his teacher once sent him home from school with a note stating, "He is too stupid to learn."

9. *TRUE or FALSE?* Mattel co-founder Ruth Handler, who created both the Barbie Doll and the Ken Doll, named the two dolls after her daughter and son (respectively, of course).

10. The modern baseball glove was invented by a spitball pitcher named Bill Doak in 1920, who licensed it to Rawlings Sporting Goods. Which National League team did Doak play for?

11. Richard Saunders was the pen name for which famous inventor?

12. There are three criteria that an inventor must meet in order to be granted a patent. What are the criteria?

13. *TRUE or FALSE?* Inventor Nikola Tesla created a man-made earthquake in Manhattan in 1898 when he found the exact frequency required to cause the earth to rumble.

14. *TRUE or FALSE?* Inventor Walt Disney sold his first work at age seven. He was also afraid of mice.

15. What is the significance of 18th-century inventors Francis Hopkinson and George Clymer?

… and the correct answers are:

The answers to each of the TRUE / FALSE questions are "TRUE." Here are the answers to the rest of the questions:

1. B (Charles Lindbergh)

2. The Lionel Train Manufacturing Company

5. He was the only inventor who worked for both Alexander Graham Bell and Thomas Edison

6. Valentine's Day

7. ice skates

8. Thomas Edison

10. St. Louis Cardinals

11. Ben Franklin; he wrote *Poor Richard's Almanack* under the pen name of Richard Saunders

12. The invention must be new; it must be "unobvious" to people in that industry; and it must be useful.

15. They both were signers of the Declaration of Independence

Who needs the Grammys or the Emmys when you have the Inventor Awards?

One of the hallmarks of greatness is having an award named after you. A number of well-known inventors have achieved this honor.

Three famous people whose names are synonymous with inventions each have an interesting bit of irony attached to their awards. The three people profiled here are Thomas Edison, Alfred Nobel and Rube Goldberg.

Thomas Edison and the Edison Medal:

Nikola Tesla was born in 1856 in Croatia, which was then a part of Yugoslavia. Tesla was a genius in two brand new industries – radio and electricity – and inventing seemed to run in his family, as his mother invented household appliances.

Tesla went to work for Thomas Edison for a year in 1883, but he and Edison had a long-running feud with over which type of electrical current was superior – Edison's DC (direct current) or Tesla's AC (alternating current). Edison had invested heavily in his DC current and he did his best to discredit Tesla. He even went so far as electrocuting animals – ranging in size from a dog to an elephant – to try to convince the public that Tesla's AC electricity was more dangerous than his own DC power.

Tesla's AC eventually won out over Edison's DC. Tesla was awarded the prestigious Edison Medal in 1917. Despite winning this award, he never received the proper recognition or respect during his lifetime. He did have an award named for him, though. The Nikola Tesla Award has been presented by the Institute of Electrical Engineers annually since 1976.

This genius inventor who held more than 700 patents in the United States and Europe died broke despite being one of the greatest electrical and radio pioneers who ever lived. Like the proverbial starving artist, Tesla's genius wasn't fully recognized until after his death.

Alfred Nobel and the Nobel Prizes:

The person whose name is attached to one of mankind's greatest awards is Alfred Nobel. The awards are divided into five classifications:

- ☀ Physics
- ☀ Chemistry
- ☀ Physiology and medicine
- ☀ Literature
- ☀ Peace

Nobel was a Swedish chemist and inventor born in 1833, the same year that his father went bankrupt. His father, also an inventor, left home to escape debtor's prison. After one of Alfred's factories blew up in 1864, killing five people, including his younger brother, he was tagged with the unfortunate nickname of "The Merchant of Death." Another factory belonging to Alfred blew up two years later.

The irony of Nobel's story is that the invention which funded the Nobel Prizes that Alfred had established was ... dynamite. Alfred, who never married, was a pacifist who didn't want a legacy associated with death. After he died in 1896, nearly all of his wealth went to the establishment of the five Nobel Prizes.

The so-called "Merchant of Death" was able to secure a positive legacy for himself with the establishment of the awards that bear his name.

Rube Goldberg and the Reuben Award:

Rube Goldberg went to college to fulfill his father's ambition of his son becoming an engineer. When Rube realized that an engineering career wasn't what he wanted, he turned to what he really loved doing – drawing. His engineering background wasn't wasted on his new career, though, as the drawings of his fictional character Professor Lucifer Butts made him a celebrity and helped assure his place in history. Goldberg earned a Pulitzer Prize in 1948.

The irony of Rube's story is that Rube, whose name is synonymous with inventions, never invented anything himself. So what is a "Rube Goldberg invention?"

It's a drawing of an elaborate scheme that shows 10 or more steps to accomplish a simple task. The award named in Rube Goldberg's honor is the National Cartoonists Society's Reuben Award, which is given out annually to the year's top cartoonist. Goldberg was the Society's first president. There are also a number of Rube Goldberg Machine Contests that are held each year, usually among engineering students, in which the challenge is to design a machine that uses the most complex process to complete a simple task.

The images of Edison, Tesla, Nobel and Goldberg have all appeared on postage stamps. The U.S. Postal Service has a policy of not showing living persons on stamps, so they honored them posthumously.

There are two reasons why 98% of patents fail

"I only want to invent things that will sell," said Thomas Edison, after his electric vote recorder worked but became a commercial failure.

The number in the headline is correct ... 98% of all patented inventions fail in the marketplace. Why do only 2% of the patents issued by the U.S. Patent Office each year produce a profit for the inventor?

We usually examine well-known inventions in these stories – the successful ones that you've heard of – but this story takes a look at the main reasons why the majority of inventions fail. I've found there are two main reasons for failure. They are:

1.   There is simply no market for some inventions, even though they may be patented. Many inventors patent their inventions before determining the likelihood of whether or not they will succeed. As a result, there are far too many patents issued each year.

Just because an inventor has been issued a patent for his gadget or gizmo doesn't mean that people are going to buy it. If that was the case, we'd all be buying patented inventions like the automatic pet petter, the Santa Claus detector, the motorized ice cream cone and the toilet seat landing lights. Each of these inventions received a patent; yet, for obvious reasons, they failed to catch on with the buying public.

Solution: Do your research to find out if a market exists for your invention before rushing off to get a patent. Don't fall in love with your invention without first considering whether your potential customers like it, too. It's their opinions that really matter.

2. Another main reason why inventions fail is because the inventor doesn't have the marketing skills necessary to get his product off the ground and into the marketplace. Inventing and marketing are two totally different skills; one is a right-brain function while the other is a left-brain function.

The creative aspects of inventing occur in the right side of the brain while the left side is responsible for logical, analytical thinking that correlates with business skills. The same pattern can be found among artists, which explains why there are so many "starving artists." Artists and inventors tend to be more creative than business-minded.

Solution: Marketing is a skill that can be learned, so spend enough time on the "business end" of your inventions. The most successful inventor in U.S. history, Thomas Edison, succeeded with his inventions because he knew how to market them.

Just as a patent does not guarantee success, not all successful inventions have been patented, either. Since this book is about inventions, I know you've been waiting anxiously to read about one certain invention, so I'll go ahead and mention it now: The Pet Rock! The Pet Rock was a huge success even though it was never patented.

For every invention that succeeds, there are 50 other inventions that fail. People often assume that just because someone has invented something or received a patent, that he'll make a fortune from it. Nothing could be further from the truth, so if you come up with your own electric vote recorder, remember the words of Thomas Alva Edison when he said, "I only want to invent things that will sell."

How the advertising exec invented a million dollar rock

"Place it on some old newspapers. The rock will require no further instruction," – from the *Pet Rock Training Manual*

"2/3 of a pun is p.u."— comments from your humble scribe's former college instructor

In 1975 a California advertising executive named Gary Dahl was telling some of his colleagues what he thought would be an ideal pet – a Pet Rock. His friends didn't consider pursuing the idea, but the 37-year old Dahl thought it had some potential. He didn't take the idea for granite – I mean granted (bad pun number one).

The Pet Rock, which isn't technically an invention, is one of the best-known fads of all time. The Pet Rock is to novelty gifts what a Rube Goldberg invention is to any type of system that requires about a dozen steps to achieve what should be a very simple task.

The Pet Rock is synonymous with inventions that made a fortune for the inventor, even though the Pet Rock technically wasn't an invention. This totally ridiculous idea succeeded because the only person who thought it made sense did a brilliant job of packaging and promoting it. Since this happened in the 1970's, it's my duty to inform you that he was not stoned (bad pun number two) when he came up with the idea.

The feature that made the Pet Rock so attractive was the instruction manual and booklet that accompanied each rock. Retailing for $3.95, each of the rocks cost Dahl about a penny apiece. The *Pet Rock Training Manual* and the gift box – shaped like a pet carrying case – are what really made it a popular item, and they also made up the majority of the production costs.

The fact that people would pay for something as simple as a rock has caused many would-be inventors to scratch their heads and ask, "Why didn't I think of that?"

The Pet Rock was originally conceived as a parody of a dog training manual, and it went on to outsell other '70's fads such as lava lamps and mood rings. It did not have the staying power of some of the best fads of the '60's such as the Slinky, the Hula Hoop or the Frisbee, though. Its meteoric rise (bad pun number three) commanded even more attention than Rubik's Cube or the Cabbage Patch Kids of the '80's.

Dahl introduced the Pet Rock at a San Francisco gift show in 1975 and began writing up orders immediately. A major reason why he was able to sell so many rocks was because he received a lot of media exposure, including:

- 💡 A half-page story in *Newsweek*

- 💡 Two appearances on *The Tonight Show with Johnny Carson*

- 💡 Stories in fl of the daily newspapers in the United States.

In fact, with all of the media exposure his Pet Rock received, I doubt if he spent a dime on advertising. He became a millionaire from his idea by selling more than a million rocks at a profit of $1.05 each. In the process, he became a legend of nearly mythical proportions. Other inventors have made a fortune with their products, but it takes a genius to squeeze a fortune out of a rock!

As is the custom with fads, the popularity of the Pet Rock fell just as quickly as it began. By early 1976, just 5 months after it hit America like an asteroid, the Pet Rock phenomenon had faded away.

Where is the inventor now?

Gary Dahl runs his own ad agency in California. He also wrote a book for the popular "Dummies" series, called "*Advertising for Dummies.*"

If you're keeping score at home, there were three really bad puns in this story and, counting the asteroid comment, one pretty good metaphor.

Was he a successful inventor, a mad scientist or a quack?

We've all heard of inventors who were considered to be quacks. You can decide for yourself if this inventor was a quack ... or if he was a genius who was years ahead of his time.

He claimed to be able to create a man-made earthquake. He considered himself to be a pioneer in radio, and he once believed that he was up for a Nobel Prize in physics.

His work attracted financial backing (a sign of a successful inventor) from the likes of George Westinghouse and J.P. Morgan. He was awarded the prestigious Edison Medal in 1917. Despite winning this award, he never received the proper recognition or respect during his lifetime, which is one reason why so few people know much about this man.

He claimed to have invented a better system of electrical current than Thomas Edison. In fact, he even worked for Edison for a year, in 1884. However, Edison would later electrocute animals with this man's technology in an attempt to prove its harmful effects.

Maybe we can get a better idea of the type of person he was by what others said about him ...

"He has contributed more to electrical science than any man up to his time," according to Lord Kelvin.

"He is an eminent pioneer in the realm of high frequency currents...

I congratulate him on the great successes of his life's work," said Albert Einstein.

Edwin Armstrong said, *"The world ... will wait a long time for his equal in achievement and imagination."*

Who is this mystery inventor? Was he a successful inventor, or was he a "mad scientist"?

His name was Nikola Tesla. He wasn't a mad scientist, although he was the inspiration for the mad scientist in Max Fleischer's Superman cartoons. And he definitely wasn't a quack. He was a genius, pure and simple; a man whose ideas were years ahead of his time. This explains why most people didn't understand his ideas in the late 1800's, and why most of us have never heard of him since.

Tesla's two greatest accomplishments were in the areas of electricity and radio.

He generated the Alternating Current power that we all use. It is Tesla's AC rather than Edison's DC which gives us electrical power over long distances. He designed the first hydroelectric power plant in Niagara Falls with his AC current in 1895.

As a radio pioneer, Tesla did more in this area than the man who is regarded as the "Father of radio" – Guglielmo Marconi. In fact, Marconi used 17 of Tesla's radio patents in his work. As a result, many of Marconi's applications were turned down. Ironically, it was also Marconi, not Tesla, who won a Nobel Prize in 1909.

As for the other claims in this story ...

Tesla claimed to be able to create a man-made earthquake because ... he actually did create a man-made earthquake! In 1898, he created a device that was about the size of an alarm clock and used it to find the exact frequency required to cause the earth to rumble – and shook Manhattan. It was the kind of experiment that you might see in a science fiction movie. Realizing that his experiment was getting out of hand, he stopped just as the police came running through his door. It was later documented in an article in the *New York American* entitled, "Tesla's Controlled Earthquakes."

Tesla also once believed that he was up for a Nobel Prize in physics because the press had reported that he and his main rival would share a Nobel Prize, but that the rival refused to accept the award with him. Who was the rival? His former boss, Thomas Edison, who he worked for in 1884. The Nobel Foundation does not back up this claim, though.

MRI's (magnetic resoning imaging) are measured in Tesla units, and the Nikola Tesla Award is named for him as well. Tesla's image is on the dollar bill in his native Croatia. He also patented the first speedometer for cars.

Tesla kept dozens of notebooks of his findings, many of which hadn't yet been put into practice by the time he died. These note-books were mysteriously taken from his home on the day he died. Tesla lived the last 30 years of his life alone. He never married and, despite his many successes, he died broke in 1943.

This inventor's mouse and duck are more than 70 years old!

Some stories tell of a person who did something spectacular in his lifetime to benefit millions of people, yet the person remains anonymous. Everyone knows his contribution but no one knows his name.

This is not one of those stories.

This is a story about a man who you've probably heard of unless you live in a cave – a man who invented something in 1937 called the multi-plane camera. Most people have never heard of the multi-plane camera, but it was the only invention this inventor ever patented. This single invention has touched the life of nearly every American, and the inventor's name is synonymous with the company he founded with his brother.

He was born in Chicago in 1901 and grew up on a farm near Marceline, Missouri. He kept a mouse and a duck alive for more than seventy years. In fact, both the mouse and the duck are alive and doing well, even though the man died in 1966.

He grew up not far from where J.C. Penney (as in the J.C. Penney department store) was born. J.C. Penney went on to amass a fortune as one of the world's most successful retailers, but our young farmboy's story is just as impressive. Farming wasn't what made him famous, though.

He began drawing at age five and sold his first works at age seven. When he was just sixteen, he wanted to join the military but was rejected because he was too young. He then joined the Red Cross and was sent overseas. He was assigned to drive an ambulance, which he covered with cartoons that he had drawn.

When he returned stateside in 1920, he moved to Kansas City to begin a career as an advertising cartoonist. A few years later, he moved to California at age twenty-two with just $40 in his pocket to join his brother and pursue his dream.

The afore-mentioned mouse and duck made him wealthy and famous during the Great Depression.

73

But let's get back to our hero's only patented invention. The multi-plane camera brought better looking, richer animation to the big screen. It fueled the imagination of its inventor/artist and allowed other artists who worked for him to expand their work. He also used it to produce *Snow White and the Seven Dwarfs* in 1937, which was the first full-length animated film to use the multi-plane camera.

Since you've probably figured out the identities of the man, the mouse and the duck by now, there's no use in stringing you along any more. We're talking about Walt Disney.

"Oh, I get it ... that's the 70-year old mouse and duck he was talking about."

Disney introduced Mickey Mouse in his second movie, *Steamboat Willie*, in 1928 and Donald Duck in *The Little Wise Hen* in 1934.

Walt Disney earned the first of his 30 Academy Awards in 1932. He also received the Medal of Freedom from President Lyndon Johnson in 1964. He and his wife Lilly had two daughters.

What's particularly inspiring about Disney is how he rose out of no-where to become an industry giant. From humble be-ginnings, the Dis-ney Corporation has made hundreds of films since Walt went to Hollywood in 1923. Including theme parks and merchandise, the Disney Corporation rings up annual sales of $22 billion.

Walt Disney was inducted into the Inventors Hall of Fame posthumously in 2000, but there's one other thing you might not have known about Walt Disney. He was afraid of mice!

These 26 inventors make our list of All-Stars, from A to Z

(This is the first in a three-part series)

Ruth or Bonds?

Marino, Elway or Montana?

Russell or Chamberlain?

While we can't settle the debate over who was the best athlete at each position, here at Invention Mysteries World Headquarters we do have the answer to the question, "Who are the greatest inventors of all time?"

Well, sort of. We went through the alphabet to determine which inventors are the best at their respective letters, and we present our unscientific findings here.

A ...

A is for Archimedes, a famous Greek mathematician and inventor born during the third century B.C. He invented the hydraulic screw, also known as the Archimedes screw, which was used in pumping water from the Nile River, as well as the worm gear, which is still used today, and the world's first winch, which he used to move a ship while it was docked on land. He also coined the word "Eureka."

B ...

Which is the more important invention ... the telephone or the World Wide Web? The answer will determine the more important inventor ... Alexander Graham Bell or Tim Berners-Lee, the inventor of the World Wide Web. This is a close call, but without the telephone, there would be no Web. Runner-up awards go to Clarence Birdseye and Karl Benz.

C ...

George Washington Carver, the pride of Missouri who was born to slave parents and invented hundreds of uses for plants, wins the letter C in a landslide. Alexander Cartwright, the likely inventor of baseball; Willis Carrier, the inventor of the air conditioner; and Chester Carlson of Xerox fame receive honorable mention.

D ...

Hmmm ... this is another tough one ... Walt Disney or Nelson Doubleday? The man who basically invented a whole new industry and is in the Inventors Hall of Fame, or the man who was once credited with inventing the great game of baseball? Actually, both men take a back seat to the great 15th century inventor and visionary, Leonardo da Vinci.

E ...

While you won't find the letter E anywhere in *Gadsby* once you get past the title, you literature buffs will remember that it was Ralph Waldo Emerson who is credited with saying, *"Necessity is the mother of invention."* (What he really said was, *"Invention breeds invention."*) The real contest here is between Thomas Alva Edison and Albert Einstein. Since this book is about inventors and inventions rather than physics, Edison owns the letter E with his 1,093 patents.

F ...

This is a tough one. How do you not award it to the main inventor of television, Philo Farnsworth, who started working on TV when he was just 15 years old? Or to Sir Alexander Fleming, whose penicillin has saved millions of lives? Either one is worthy, but surpassing them both is multi-talented inventor Benjamin Franklin.

G ...

Al Gore invented the letter G ... no, wait, it was the Internet that he invented. Due to a technicality (the pesky little fact that he didn't really invent it) we award the letter to Johannes Gutenberg for inventing the printing press. In a three-way tie for second place are Charles Goodyear, Wilson Greatbatch, who invented the implantable pacemaker, and our favorite non-inventor, cartoonist Rube Goldberg.

H ...

Ruth Handler or Hippocrates? Handler's company, Mattel, has sold more than a billion Barbie Dolls, but anyone who has an oath named after him gets my vote. He gets bonus points for being recognizable by only his first name while not acting like a diva like other one-name stars, i.e. Cher, Madonna, Fabio, etc.

Since all good things come in three's (The 3 Wise Men; Peter, Paul and Mary; The 3 Stooges; A Priest, a Rabbi and a Nun; etc.), we'll break this list into three parts. Read about our letter-winning All-Star inventors from I – Z in the next two stories.

These All-Star inventors owr middle of the alphabet

(This is the second in a three-part series)

I ...

There are plenty of inventions that begin with the letter ı, such as ice cream, instant photography, the internal combustion engine and the Internet (see Al Gore in the previous story), but the staff here at Invention Mysteries World Headquarters had to search far and wide to find an inventor – any inventor – whose name begins with "I."

The Indians of the Navajo tribe invented the secret code that they used to encode and decode messages to help the Allies win World War II. Actually, the secret code was their own language, and the code talkers were instrumental in every major battle in the Pacific, including Iwo Jima. They were also the basis of the 2002 movie, *"Windtalkers."*

J ...

The greatest presidential inventor in United States history owns the letter J. Thomas Jefferson invented a moldboard plow, a wheel cipher, a spherical sundial, a portable copying press, automatic double doors, the swivel chair, the dumbwaiter and a macaroni machine. He also introduced french fries, ice cream, waffles, and macaroni to the U.S. He helped establish the U.S. Patent Office in 1790.

K ...

Dean Kamen is an inventor from New Hampshire whose medical inventions include the first portable insulin pump and the heart stent used to repair the heart of Vice President Dick Cheney. His transportation inventions include a wheelchair called iBot, which allows users to climb stairs and raise themselves upright, and a gyroscope-based scooter called the Segway

...ransporter, which made national headlines a few years

...ond place goes to Margaret Knight, whose invention of the
...at-bottomed grocery bag in 1871 has stood the test of time for
more than 130 years.

L ...

There's probably no inventor who surrounded himself with better
company than Lewis Latimer, who was the only inventor who
worked with both Alexander Graham Bell and Thomas Edison.
William Lear, though, held more than 100 patents in aviation and
electronics, including the world's first working car radio, which he
co-invented and sold to Motorola. He also invented the eight-track
tape player. Disco lives!

M ...

There's a lot of competition for the letter M, starting with fictional TV character MacGyver (whose mysterious first name of Angus
was only revealed during the series' final season). MacGyver could
make something out of practically anything, but he loses on a technicality – the fact that he was a fictional TV character. So the award
for those whose names being with M goes to Samuel Morse, inventor of the Morse code and the telegraph which linked the East
Coast and West Coast in 1861. A distant third-place prize goes to
the inventor of the do-over in golf, David Mulligan, whose name
is called out by cheaters everywhere.

N ...

On the one hand, you have Alfred Nobel, inventor of dynamite
and some pretty cool awards. On the other hand, you have the
inventor of the game of basketball, Dr. James Naismith. Call me
superstitious, but I just don't think it's a good idea to upset the person who invented dynamite, so we award the letter N to Nobel.

O ...

The Olson Twins. No, not Mary-Kate and Ashley. We're talking about the hockey-playing Olson Brothers — Scott and Brennan — who invented Rollerblades. The Olson name is derived from the Scandinavian word which means "ancestor's relic." How ironic, considering the oldest-known ancestor to Rollerblades was a relic made by nailing wooden spools to strips of wood and attaching them to shoes. Coincidence or conspiracy? I'll let you decide. (P.S. The brothers are not twins.)

Here are the remaining All-Star inventors, from P to Z

(This is the third in a three-part series)

P ...

This is a tough one. Is it ...

a. The inventor of Coca-Cola, Dr. Pemberton?

b. The inventor of Kool-Aid, Edwin Perkins?

c. James Paige, who received a patent for the Paige Typesetter, which was funded by one of our favorite inventors, Mark Twain?

d. Robert Patch, who invented and patented a toy truck that could be changed into different types of trucks? What's so great about that, you say? Mr. Patch was only six years old when he received his patent.

e. None of the above.

The winner is "None of the above" because of chemist Louis Pasteur's process of pasteurization. Case closed.

Q ...

Q is for Q, the fictional inventor in the James Bond series. As a rule, we disqualify fictional characters in our list of A – Z All-Stars on a technicality (see fictional TV character MacGyver in the previous section), but since there are no well-known actual inventors whose names begin with Q (also see U and X), this technicality becomes a technicality itself and, like a double negative, it cancels itself out. So the Q goes to Q.

R ...

Dr. Robert Rines, inventor of high definition radar and the imaging sonar used in sonograms, is one of the world's top experts on the Loch Ness Monster, and he uses his own sonar technology to search for the legendary Monster. Your humble scribe had the opportunity to visit his office recently and see first-hand photos taken nearly 30 years ago of what appeared to be the Monster. (Nessie's fins are much bigger in the photos than in the usual images.) Dr. Rines's technology was also used to find the *Titanic* and the *Bismarck*, and he holds more than 60 patents.

S ...

Eighteen-year-old Ralph Samuelson from Minnesota invented waterskiing in 1922 after he figured that if you could ski on snow, then you could ski on water. Then there's Levi Strauss, who deserves some consideration for creating blue jeans, but the winner is Igor Sikorsky, inventor of the helicopter.

T ...

Croatian-born inventor Nikola Tesla was one of the most inventive geniuses of all time. Tesla is the main developer of two of the world's most important inventions or discoveries — radio and alternating current electricity (a.k.a. AC), even though most of the world has never heard of him.

U ...

NEXT!!!

V ...

Oh, Vanna, do we have a V for the inventor of the vacuum, Otto Von Guericke, the former Burgermeister of Madgeburg, Germany? Von Guericke served as the town's Burgermeister (mayor) during the 1600's.

W ...

The Brothers Wright – Wilbur and Orville – for the patent they received for their "flying machine." 'Nuff said.

X ...

NEXT!!!

Y ...

Gumpei Yokoi, creator of the Nintendo Game Boy.

Z ...

You wouldn't think that there would be much competition for the letter Z, but there's Frank Zamboni, inventor of the ice-resurfacing machine that bears his name and Ferdinand Zeppelin, who invented the dirigible which he named after himself. But Russian immigrant Vladimir Zworykin invented the cathode-ray tube needed for television transmission. Zworykin also invented the iconoscope, an early television camera. Even though kids probably watch way too much TV, we still award the letter Z to Vladimir Zworykin.

Here's a re-cap of the letter-winning inventors in this 3-part series, from A to Z, excluding U and X:
Archimedes
Alexander Graham Bell
George Washington Carver
Leonardo da Vinci
Thomas Edison
Benjamin Franklin
Johannes Gutenberg
Hippocrates
Indians of the Navajo tribe
Thomas Jefferson

Dean Kamen
William Lear
Samuel Morse
Alfred Nobel
Scott and Brennan Olson
Louis Pasteur
Q
Robert Rines
Igor Sikorsky
Nikola Tesla
Otto Von Guericke
Wilbur and Orville Wright
Gumpei Yokoi
Vladimir Zworykin

Now for the $64,000 question: Of the 26 inventors in this 3-part series, how many are still living?

Only four: The Navajo Indians (although the last of the code talkers died in 2004); Dean Kamen; Scott and Brennan Olson; and Robert Rines.

Four inventors signed the Declaration of Independence

In 1776, while working for our nation's independence from England, Benjamin Franklin said, "Indeed we must all hang together, otherwise we will hang separately." The penalty for treason against the British was death by hanging.

We celebrate our nation's freedom by taking a look at two signers of the Declaration of Independence who were also known as inventors in their day. Ben Franklin and Thomas Jefferson — two of the most famous among the 56 signers — were inventors, but there were two other signers who were inventors but who are unknown to most Americans.

Francis Hopkinson:

Francis Hopkinson (1737 - 1791) was born in Philadelphia. His father was one of the first trustees of the College of Philadelphia (now known as the University of Pennsylvania) as well as its first graduate. Hopkinson went on to become a judge.

The only "inventions" that Judge Hopkinson created were the American flag and the Great Seal of the United States. While history credits Betsy Ross with designing the flag, it was probably Hopkinson who played the larger role in its design. Betsy Ross had sewn the flag together, and this may be why she is regarded as the person who designed the flag. The journals of the Continental Congress indicate that Hopkinson designed the flag, though. In 2000, the U.S. Postal Service issued a stamp in honor of Hopkinson's flag design.

In addition to being an inventor, Hopkinson was also an author and he wrote a ballad called *The Battle of the Kegs* in 1778. The ballad was loosely based on a battle in which gunpowder kegs floated down the Delaware River toward the British at Philadelphia, and the British returned the favor by firing back. Hopkinson was also a chemist, a physicist, a musician, a composer and an artist.

George Clymer:

Like Hopkinson, George Clymer (1739 - 1813) was born in Pennsylvania. He was an orphan raised by his uncle, and his paternal ancestors were among the earliest settlers of the state.

Clymer invented the Colombian printing press, which was an improvement over Ben Franklin's printing press. But the Columbian, with all its bells and whistles, never caught on in the United States.

You may have heard the story of how the signers of the Declaration of Independence were hunted by the British for treason. The 56 signers literally risked everything fighting for our nation's freedom. Each one became a marked man. Some were captured, while others, like Thomas Jefferson, escaped.

Nine of the signers died during the war, but all were driven from their homes at one time or another. Five were captured, imprisoned and abused. Seventeen signers lost everything they owned, including twelve whose homes were completely burned. Several lost their wives and families. One lost all 13 of his children.

George Clymer and Francis Hopkinson both escaped with their families, but their properties were completely destroyed. Clymer was the only signer who returned to England. His reason for returning was that England presented him with a better opportunity for his Colombian printing press.

Thomas Jefferson died on the 4th of July, 1826, exactly 50 years after the Declaration of Independence was adopted. Coincidentally, it was the same day that another signer, John Adams, died.

In the end, each of the 56 signers kept his word to "... mutually pledge to each other our lives, our fortunes and our sacred honor."

A craving for ice cream led to the invention of the outboard motor

One night during the summer of 2001, I received a phone call from the marina where I had docked my boat in storage just three days earlier. The boat was nothing fancy — just a little 16-foot boat that I used for skiing, but it had a huge 115-horsepower motor that looked totally out of place on such a small boat.

That motor doubled the weight of the boat. Okay, that's not exactly true. It tripled the weight.

I referred to the motor as a Binford 6000. Binford was the fictional sponsor on the TV show *Home Improvement*, and anything that has more power than normal is often referred to as a "Binford."

The call from the marina that fateful night went something like this:

Marina person: "Mr. Niemann, your boat sunk."

Me: (in a state of shock) "WHAT?!?"

Marina person: (louder) "Mr. Niemann, your boat sunk."

Me: "I heard you the first time." (After calming down a little) "Well, that's not so bad. How's the Binford 6000?"

Marina person: "Bad news, Sir. I'm afraid the motor went down with the ship."

Me: (in another state of shock) "WHAT?!?"

Marina person: (louder) "Bad news, Sir. I'm afraid the motor went down with the ship."

The next day I called my brother to help me pull it out, and told him to bring ropes, a pulley, a winch, whatever he could find.

So he brought a camera.

"This looks like a Kodak moment, and I want to get this on film," he said. I think he wanted evidence in case I ever denied that my boat sunk.

After he took several pictures of me standing next to my little *Titanic*, we pulled it out of the water and towed it over to shore. After draining all the water out and towing it home, I looked for the cause of the leak. The caulking around the back side of the boat had worn off, and while it didn't cause any problems when I took it out on the Mississippi River for a couple hours at a time, it couldn't handle 3 days of constantly being in the water at the marina.

Not willing to spend the money that it would take to get it fixed, I was fortunate to find a mechanic who wanted to buy it despite the fact that it didn't run anymore. Actually, I think he just wanted the Binford 6000 motor and not the rest of that old boat.

The whole incident, which I've been unable to forget even though it didn't leave any psychological scars, made me think about how the Binford motor – uh, make that the outboard motor – was invented. It turns out that the Girlfriend (rather than the Mother) of Necessity was the inspiration behind this invention.

"Don't row! Throw the oars away"
...The inventor's ad writer, Bess, in an ad promoting his new invention: the outboard motor

In 1906, a 29-year-old immigrant from Norway named Ole took his girlfriend for a picnic near a Wisconsin lake. She hinted that she wanted some ice cream, so Ole rowed his boat across the river to find her some ice cream. When the ice cream began to melt by the time he returned, he figured there must be a quicker way to power the boat. In fact, it was during this trip that he figured out that a boat might be able to use a gas engine.

Ole came to America with his family when he was just five. At age 10, he quit school to work on the family farm. He had read about the internal combustion engine, and was no doubt inspired by its potential and its applications.

When Ole was 15, he built two boats. Why two boats? Because

his father, who had lost three uncles at sea, chopped the first boat to bits. Ole had never sailed before, but his boat worked just fine. He was as well-qualified to design the outboard motor as anyone.

What was his last name?

You guessed it: Evinrude. Like many other inventors whose products created an entirely new industry, Ole Evinrude created a whole new industry with his invention. And the person who inspired him to invent it, his girlfriend Bess, soon became his wife. His company later merged into the Outboard Marine Corporation.

I'm guessing that Ole probably checked his boat's caulking before he stored it in the marina.

This inventor had a killer working for him in 1804

While the above headline might not sound all that interesting at first, wait until you learn the identities of the inventor, the killer and the victim. Each one was known for something other than their main profession, and each one left a lasting legacy that has something to do with money some 200 years later.

First, the inventor ...

He helped establish the United States Patent Office in 1790. Oddly enough, he was originally against the idea of patents because he considered patents to be an unfair monopoly.

But that isn't what he was known for. So who was this inventor?

We'll call him Tom, because his name was Tom.

His inventions included the swivel chair, a new type of sundial, the moldboard plow and the cipher wheel. Among his peers at his main job, he was without equal as an inventor. Tom also introduced French fries, ice cream, waffles and macaroni to the United States. In fact, he invented a macaroni machine.

But that isn't what Tom was known for. So what was his claim to fame?

Tom has several legacies larger than his inventions ... such as serving as our nation's first patent commissioner, his Monticello estate, establishing the University of Virginia, serving as Secretary of State and serving as president of the United States. That's right, Tom is Thomas Jefferson. His name and image appear on the $2 bill.

Next, for the killer who worked for him ...

But first, one more annoying question, and then I'll stop. I promise. Who was the killer who worked for Thomas Jefferson, our nation's third president?

In 1799, he founded the Bank of the Manhattan Company, which later merged with another bank to become Chase Manhattan Bank, but that's not what he is remembered for.

I can't reveal his name just yet because that would give it away, but he killed a man in a pistol duel that made headlines at the time. In fact, it caused a national outrage, as the victim was a signer of the Declaration of Independence. The man who worked for President Thomas Jefferson and also founded the company that became Chase Manhattan Bank was initially indicted for murder, but the charge was later reduced and he served no prison time. A year later, he finished the job for which he was elected ... serving as Thomas Jefferson's vice president. That man, of course, is Aaron Burr.

Finally, the victim ...

The loser of that duel, Alexander Hamilton, became regarded as a hero or, as the NRA once said, "a lousy shot." (In some duels, the two combatants would fire their pistols at trees, intentionally missing the other person. This allowed each person to save face without killing his opponent.) Hamilton had his image placed on the $10 bill, while Burr's reputation is still tarnished two centuries later.

Who were they before they were inventors?

The inventor of the vacuum, Otto Von Guericke of Madgeburg, Germany, served as his town's mayor from 1646 to 1676. A mayor was also referred to as the "Burgermeister" back then and there. (On a separate but equally important note, I would like to officially be known as the "Writermeister" from now on. That's with a capital "W.")

This made me wonder what other inventors had significant jobs in addition to their careers as inventors. It turns out that there were quite a few, including some whose other jobs, or "previous lives," were more significant than their careers as inventors.

For example, the inventor of the perfusion pump that keeps the heart and other organs alive outside of the body during surgery is known not for this invention but rather for his main career ... as a pioneering aviator in the 1920's and 1930's. Who was this inventor? Charles Lindbergh.

In 1849, an Illinois inventor received a patent for "A Device for Buoying Vessels Over Shoals." He went on to become one of our nation's greatest presidents ... Abraham Lincoln. He's also the only U.S. president to receive a patent.

The funding that enabled an inventor named Alfred Nobel to establish the Nobel prizes came from the invention of ... dynamite. Nobel was a pacifist who didn't want a legacy associated with death, and he assured himself of a better legacy with the awards that bear his name.

The Jacuzzi brothers immigrated to America around 1917 and built aviation equipment before turning their attention to building – go to the back of the class if you get this one wrong – jacuzzis. A fatal crash of one of the planes they designed led them to make the switch. Candido Jacuzzi ran the family business until 1969, when he was indicted for income-tax evasion and returned to Italy.

The next time you adjust your radio dial, you can thank Hedy Lamarr. Who? Hedy was a silver-screen actress during the 1930's and 1940's. If you're too young to remember her (as I am), ask your parents. If they're too young, have them ask their parents. The "Secret Communication System" that she co-invented manipulated radio frequencies and was intended to prevent the Nazis from intercepting radio-guided torpedoes in World War II. The technology is similar to what happens when you hit the "scan" button on your car radio. The Navy, by the way, rejected her Secret Communication System in World War II, but her technology is used in cell phones today and in radio.

Speaking of actors, there are others who have lived "previous lives" who were not inventors. For example, one actor received a $9,000 check for a movie that he appeared in, and he carried the check around with him to show to his friends. By the time he went to cash it, the film company had gone bankrupt, causing the check to bounce! That actor was Babe Ruth.

The list goes on and on, but we'll conclude with the story of another actor – this one from a small town in Illinois who went on to serve as president of the Screen Actors Guild, then as governor of California, and finally as the person most responsible for ending communism in Europe and the Soviet Union while he served as the 40th President of the United States … Ronald Reagan.

Even though President Reagan was a great man, he wasn't an inventor.

Learn the origins of our favorite summertime inventions

Have you ever wondered where all of those great summertime inventions came from? You know, the things that make summer what it is; like baseball, ice cream and swimming.

The staff here at I.M.W.H. (that's Invention Mysteries World Headquarters) decided to dig up some evidence about the origins of our favorite summertime inventions. Here's what we found:

Ice Cream

The origin of ice cream is uncertain, but it was probably invented in China approximately 4,000 years ago – I think it was on a Wednesday around 2:00 p.m. Fast forward to the 1600's, when King Charles I of England enjoyed ice cream on a regular basis, freshly prepared by his chef. In fact, he had his chef keep the recipe a secret.

After he was beheaded in 1649 (Charles I of England, not the chef because they usually don't do that to chefs), the chef went public with the formula. Ice cream's U.S. origins began in the 1700's when a very successful inventor named Thomas Jefferson (yes, that Thomas Jefferson) introduced it to America.

Nancy Johnson developed the first hand-crank ice cream maker in 1847. She received a patent for it and sold her rights to William Young for $200, which was pretty good money in those days. Young named the machine after the inventor, calling it the "Johnson Patent Ice-Cream Freezer."

The ice cream cone could have been invented by a number of different ice cream vendors; the only thing we know for sure is that it first became popular at the World's Fair in St. Louis in 1904.

Baseball

Baseball's rules were created by bank clerk Alexander Cartwright, although he may have based his version of the game partially on an earlier version by Nelson Doubleday. Doubleday, who fired the first shot in defense of the Union during the Civil War, was long credited for inventing the game of baseball.

Nearly every major league sports team has a Gatorade cooler near the bench. Gatorade was invented in 1965 by Dr. Robert Cade, a medical researcher at the University of Florida. One of the school's football coaches wanted a way to keep his players performing well in the hot weather, so he asked the team doctor, who worked with Dr. Cade, for help.

After trying a number of different formulas, they came up with what became known as Gatorade. Why Gatorade? The school's team name is the "Gators." Gatorade exploded onto the market when the football team won their first Orange Bowl in 1967, and the sports drink now rings up billions of dollars in sales annually. Incidentally, Cade had offered the rights to his Gatorade patent to the school, but it turned him down. Big mistake.

Swimming

What would summer be without swimming? The inventor of the bikini, Louis Reard, named it after the Bikini Islands in the Pacific Ocean in 1945, near the end of World War II. You would think that he came up with the name after seeing women wearing the little two-piece swimsuit there, but that's not the case. It's a mystery why he named it the bikini, but it may have had something to with a major event that happened nearby — the explosion of the world's first nuclear bomb.

The bikini led to the need for sunscreen, which was invented by Miami Beach pharmacist Benjamin Green in 1944, who created it to protect soldiers serving in the South Pacific. Green brewed his successful formula of cocoa butter and jasmine on his wife's stove and, being bald, he tested it on his own head. The sunscreen that he developed became known as Coppertone.

Green had competition, though, when 25-year-old high school teacher and part-time lifeguard Ron Rice concocted his own natural tanning formula of coconut, avocado, kukui and other secret natural oils in his garage and named it Hawaiian Tropic. Rice began selling Hawaiian Tropic in 1969 on the beaches of Florida; that sounds like the perfect summer job!

We could go on and talk about many more summertime inventions, but this covers some of the main ones that we use every summer.

Who invented the Olympic Games?

"Let me win. But if I cannot win, let me be brave in the attempt" – Special Olympics motto

The very first Olympic Games took place in 776 B.C. in Olympia, Greece, hence the name "Olympics." Each of the winners of the first Olympic Games received an olive tree wreath and a hero's return to their city-states. Victory was considered to be the highest honor a mortal could attain. Three-time winners became exempt from taxation and they were honored with statues representing them. Special coins were made to commemorate equestrian victories.

Only four sports have been featured at every modern Olympic Games, which began in 1896: Track and field, fencing, weightlifting and cycling. Others, such as tug of war, rugby, polo, lacrosse, and golf were once played in the Olympics but have since been discontinued.

In this story, we examine four sports of the Summer Olympics with interesting origins, which means that we leave out any coverage of our favorite team – the Jamaican Bobsled Team. Here's a brief primer on the origins of several popular Olympic sports:

The Modern Pentathlon:

A pentathlon is a competition consisting of five events. Before we get to the modern Pentathlon, we have to go back to the ancient Pentathlon, which made its debut in 708 B.C. The ancient Pentathlon included the discus throw, the javelin, the long jump, the stadium-length race and wrestling.

The modern Pentathlon was introduced in the Stockholm Olympic Games of 1912 by the founder of the modern Olympic Games, Baron Pierre de Coubertin. Barely resembling the ancient Pentathlon, modern Pentathlon contestants must shoot, fence, swim, compete in showjumping and run.

Why these five events? Legend has it that a young cavalry officer was ordered to deliver a message on horseback. The officer had to fend off the enemy with his sword and pistol, but his horse was shot in the process, leaving him to swim and run the rest of the way to deliver the message.

Beach Volleyball:

This 2-on-2 sport traces its origin back to California in the 1920's with six players on each side. Beach volleyball was played in France as early as 1927, and spread to Bulgaria, the former Czechoslovakia and the former USSR a few years later. American soldiers helped spread it to even more countries during World War II. Matches played with two people per team first occurred in 1930. Beach volleyball made its Olympic debut at the 1996 Summer Games in Atlanta, and today it is one of the most popular events at the Olympics.

Table Tennis:

The exact origin of table tennis is unknown, but it's believed that it was first played by using cigar-box lids for paddles and a carved champagne cork for a ball. The sport was originally named "ping pong" because of the sound the ball makes when it hits the table. Table tennis debuted at the Seoul Olympics in 1988.

Football/Soccer:

While games involving the kicking of a ball have been around for thousands of years, modern soccer, known everywhere outside of America as football, originated in England during the eighth century. English sailors spread the game worldwide in the 1800's. Today, it is the most popular sport in the world.

Soccer (sorry, but I just can't get used to calling it football) made its Olympic debut as a demonstration sport in the 1896 Athens Olympics. It became an official Olympic sport in the 1908 London Olympics, and it took only 88 years for the women's game to be included in the Olympics, at the 1996 Atlanta Games, where the American women's team won the Gold Medal.

P.S.   If you're interested in volunteering to work with the Special Olympics, please visit www.SpecialOlympics.org or call (202) 628-3630 for information.

Which inventor said it?
Find out by taking the quiz

"To invent, you need a good imagination and a pile of junk" – Thomas Edison

It's time once again for another invention quiz. This one deals with invention-related quotes. A few non-inventors even found their way into this quiz with their quotes.

As is the case with all of the quizzes, the answers are at the end of the story, and each answer is used only once.

Choose from the following possible answers …

Alexander Graham Bell
Thomas Edison
Albert Einstein
Rutherford B. Hayes
Charles Kettering
Samuel Morse
Mark Twain

Agatha Christie
Wilbur Wright
Ralph Waldo Emerson
Lord Kelvin
Abraham Lincoln
Isaac Newton

Roman Engineer Julius Sextus Frontinus in 10 A.D.
patent commissioner Charles Duell

1. We'll start off with an easy one: Who said, *"What hath God wrought?"* Actually, he didn't say it but he did transmit it over the telegraph that he invented.

2. *"Watson, come here. I need you."*

3. The only American inventor to receive 1,000 patents said this: *"Of all my inventions, I liked the phonograph best. Life's most soothing things are sweet music and a child's goodnight."*

4. This is an easy one to get wright: *"I confess that in 1901 I said … that man would not fly for fifty years."*

5. Originally known as Sam, this midwestern inventor was better known for his writings than his inventions. He showed his high appreciation for inventors when he said, *"Inventors are the creators of the world – after God."*

6. This 19th century writer is credited with the quote, *"Necessity is the mother of invention."* (What he really said was, *"Invention breeds invention."*)

7. This 19th century president said this about Alexander Graham Bell's telephone: *"That's an amazing invention, but who would ever want to use one of them?"*

8. When in Rome, do as the Romans do: *"Inventions have long since reached their limit, and I see no hope for further developments."*

9. *"Everything that can be invented has already been invented."* There's a bit of irony in this one, given the man's job title.

10. As the only U.S. president to receive a patent, he said that the patent system *"added the fuel of interest to the fire of genius, in the discovery and production of new and useful things."*

11. *"People think of the inventor as a screwball, but no one ever asks the inventor what he thinks of other people."*

12. This inventor further proved that all things are relative when he said, *"No amount of experimentation can ever prove me right; a single experiment can prove me wrong."*

13. *"I don't think necessity is the mother of invention,"* she said, possibly when riding the Orient Express.

14. He didn't invent the apple, but he did discover gravity. He also said, *"If I had seen farther than most men, it is by standing on the shoulders of giants."*

15. In 1895, the inventor of the Kelvin scale said, *"Heavier-than-air flying machines are impossible."* Get this one wrong and you have to start over. (Bonus points if you know what the Kelvin scale is.)

Answers:

1. Samuel Morse
2. Alexander Graham Bell
3. Thomas Edison
4. Wilbur Wright
5. Mark Twain
6. Ralph Waldo Emerson
7. Rutherford B. Hayes
8. Roman Engineer Julius Sextus Frontinus
9. patent commissioner Charles Duell
10. Abraham Lincoln
11. Charles Kettering
12. Albert Einstein
13. Agatha Christie
14. Isaac Newton
15. Lord Kelvin

And the bonus question that was in Question 15: The Kelvin scale is the absolute temperature scale, which measures the lowest possible temperature in the universe at a negative 273 degrees Celsius.

Who were Fahrenheit, Celsius, Doppler and Richter?

Who invented the Richter scale? Or the Fahrenheit scale? This sounds like a "Who's buried in Grant's tomb?" joke, but it's no joke. People named Richter, Doppler, Fahrenheit and Celsius really did exist, and they invented devices to help people measure heat, cold and the weather.

Fahrenheit and Celsius lived mostly during the 1700's, Doppler lived during the 1800's and Richter lived during the 1900's. You know what they invented because they became household names, so here's the scoop on each inventor.

Fahrenheit

Physicist Gabriel Farenheit (1686 - 1736) was born in Danzig, Poland, which is now Gdansk. He invented the first mercury

thermometer in 1714, and then developed the first accurate thermometer ten years later. Along with his improved thermometer, Fahrenheit introduced the temperature scale that bears his name. At the time, there were already 19 other temperature scales being used.

In addition to determining that water boils at 212 degrees and freezes at 32 degrees, Fahrenheit discovered that every liquid has its own unique boiling point. Americans use the Fahrenheit scale, but people who live in countries that use the metric system use the Celsius scale.

Celsius

Astronomy Professor Anders Celsius (1701 - 1744) was born in Uppsala, Sweden. He created what was originally known as the Centigrade scale in 1742 and named his scale – which contained 100 degrees, or steps – the "Centigrade" scale because the word "centi" means "hundred" and "grade" means "steps" in Latin.

Celsius figured that the point at which water freezes must be the same temperature at which snow melts. He would often stick a mercury thermometer (which Fahrenheit had invented earlier) in the snow and measure the temperature at which the snow melted.

Oddly enough, his original scale showed zero degrees as the boiling point of water and 100 degrees as the freezing point. The scale was reversed the following year so that zero degrees became known as the freezing point and 100 degrees as the boiling point. The name of his scale was changed from Centigrade to Celsius in 1948.

Doppler

Physicist Christian Doppler (1803 – 1853) was born in Salzberg, Austria. You're probably familiar with the term "Doppler radar" because the weatherman uses it on the weather reports.

In 1842, Doppler explained the "Doppler effect." An easy way to understand the Doppler effect is by noticing the difference in the sound of a train's whistle (or a police siren, ambulance, etc.) as it moves farther away – the pitch increases as the vehicle moves toward you and decreases as it moves away from you. This was later shown to work with light as well. Today, Doppler radar is used to help predict the weather, as it can see the winds inside of storms, making it helpful in locating and predicting the arrival of tornadoes.

Richter

Seismologist Charles Richter (1900 - 1985) was born in Hamil-ton, Ohio. His Richter scale measures the height of the seismic waves released during an earthquake. One misconception that people have regarding the Richter scale is that it's actually an instrument or device. The Richter scale is actually a series of tables and charts that correlate the scale to the seismogram readings; the machine that shows the results is called a seismograph.

The numbers on the Richter scale measure the earthquake in ten-fold units, meaning that an earthquake that registers a five is 10 times more powerful than one that registers a four, one that registers a four is 10 times more powerful than one that registers a three, and so on.

Another misconception about the Richter scale is that 10 is the highest possible measure of an earthquake. In reality, the Richter scale is an open-ended scale, and while it is possible to hit a 10, it has never happened since the scale was first introduced in 1935. The Richter scale has also been used to measure the strength of quakes on the moon and Mars.

And that pretty much covers it!

Is war the stepmother of invention?

(This is the first in a two-part series)

It's common knowledge that weapons such as machine guns, hand grenades and tanks were invented to help countries win wars. In fact, wartime inventions go all the way back to the second century B.C. when the Greek mathematician and inventor Archimedes invented the catapult.

As the news is filled with coverage of the war on terror every day, the staff here at Invention Mysteries World Headquarters wondered if any beneficial inventions have ever resulted from war. It turns out that there have been quite a few.

While writing this story, I remembered the "combination spoon and can opener" that hangs on my Dad's basement wall to this day as a memento from his service in the Korean War. Like the inventions profiled in this story, that invention was probably born out of necessity. Unlike the inventions in this story, though, it didn't have a useful purpose once the war was over.

Would you rather ride in a 2-wheel or a 4-wheel "vehicle"?

It probably comes as no surprise that the first ambulance system in the United States was a direct result of war. Or that a government official was against the system before he was for it. The surprising part is that the war that gave us the ambulance was the Civil War.

The Union's medical director, Jonathan Letterman, established the first ambulance system at the start of the war to transport injured soldiers to the field hospitals. The nation's first trial lawyer was right behind that very first ambulance.

Unlike modern ambulances, those used in the Civil War were drawn by horses since motor vehicles had not been invented yet. Later ambulances used railroads and steamships to transport the wounded soldiers; some boats were even remade as floating hospitals. Just as today, the earliest ambulances were outfitted with medical supplies, and those who were not able or willing to fight ran the ambulance system.

Supply wagons were also used as ambulances following major battles. They weren't the most comfortable means of transportation, but at least the floors were covered with hay.

In the 1950's, the United States began using helicopters as ambulances during the Korean War.

The General-Purpose Vehicle:

Originally known as the "General Purpose Vehicle" and then as the G.P. for short, the JEEP's powerful engine, four-wheel drive and deep-treaded tires helped soldiers navigate through all types of terrain in World War II.

Just before the war began, the U.S. government called on 135 American car companies to create a prototype for what would become the JEEP. It took the tiny American Bantam Car Company only seven weeks to produce the winning prototype, but the U.S. Army awarded the contract to the larger Willys Truck Company and Ford Motor Company. To add insult to injury, the contract called for Willys and Ford to produce the JEEP based on Bantam's original design.

Just how big a role did the JEEP play in World War II?

General Dwight Eisenhower said that America could not have won the war without it.

Free O.J.!

We depart from the theme of vehicles with our third wartime invention. No, this segment is not about a white Ford Bronco, but rather frozen concentrate orange juice.

What's so important about frozen concentrate orange juice?

It's simple when you think about it. Soldiers were inflicted with scurvy all year round, but orange juice — which helped prevent scurvy — was only available during the warmer months.

Dr. Edwin Moore led a team that developed the frozen concentrate during World War II. Despite the importance of their work, they received no royalties for their discovery because they were working for the U.S. government at the time.

We'll take a look at more war-related inventions in the next story, including the one that saved more than a million lives since World War II, even though it was discovered by accident.

More wartime inventions
that benefit mankind

(This is the second in a two-part series)

As we discovered in the last story, war has produced many popular inventions that we take for granted. These include aerosol cans, food preservation, synthetic rubber, Silly Putty (yes, Silly Putty), jet engines, rockets and radar.

We continue where we left off by taking a look at three additional important wartime inventions, including one that has saved millions of lives since it was discovered by accident in 1928.

The "Data Translating Apparatus," also known as secret "Project PX" ...

During World War II the U. S. Army awarded a grant to inventors John Mauchly and John Eckert, Jr. to build a device to help the war effort. Originally labeled as Project PX, the ENIAC, which stands for Electronic Numerical Integrator and Computer, was the first electronic digital computer. It is also the system to which modern computers trace their roots.

Within two years, the ENIAC was able to predict the weather, calculate atomic energy and study wind tunnel design, along with many other uses. It stood 150 feet long, weighed over 30 tons, contained 18,000 vacuum tubes and required 200 people to operate it. Yet it was still 1,000 times faster than previous calculators.

The war ended by the time the ENIAC was introduced to the public in 1946. Mauchly and Eckert then went on to develop the first commercial computer, the UNIVAC (which stands for UNIVersal Automatic Computer). Both inventors were inducted into the National Inventors Hall of Fame posthumously in 2002.

"Oh, I see they've got the Internet on computers now" – Homer Simpson

Staying on the theme of computers, ARPA, which stands for Advanced Research Projects Agency (enough with the acronyms already!), produced the forerunner to the Internet, known as ARPAnet. The need for the Internet was inspired by war – the Cold War – because the United States government was concerned that a nuclear attack could wipe out our intelligence system.

Here's an abbreviated version of how the Internet evolved: ARPA was created by the U.S. Department of Defense as part of the U.S. reaction to the Soviet Union's 1957 launch of Sputnik. By 1969, computer scientists had begun work on the ARPAnet, which was a network of huge supercomputers from five major universities that could exchange information with each other.

The National Science Foundation, or NSFnet, linked them together and eventually replaced the slower ARPAnet in 1990. I think you know where we're going with this. NSFnet formed the backbone of today's Internet, and the rest is history.

It took only four years for the Internet to reach 50 million users in the United States. By comparison, radio took 38 years, television took 13 years and personal computers took 16 years to reach critical mass.

Genius + Luck = The Accidental Discovery ...

Penicillin began saving lives in 1943 when two men – neither of whom were named Fleming – figured out how to produce it as an antibiotic.

Scottish scientist Sir Alexander Fleming discovered penicillin in 1928 by accident when he left his lab for a two-week vacation and returned to find that a mold had developed on a plate of staphylococcus culture. After further research, he found that the mold had stopped the bacteria from spreading. Even though the entire world knows about his discovery, it went virtually unknown for more than ten years.

It wasn't until two other men, Howard Florey and Earnest Chain, figured out how to produce penicillin as an antibiotic in 1939 that it actually benefited society. Florey and Chain had researched Fleming's work to study ways to use molds to kill bacteria. Even though they knew how to produce it as an antibiotic, they weren't able to have the drug mass-produced in Great Britain. In 1941, Florey flew to America with another colleague and got U.S. assistance for its production once the U.S. entered the war.

By the end of World War II, penicillin had begun saving millions of lives and also led to the discovery of many other antibiotics that are used today. Fleming, Florey and Chain split the 1945 Nobel Prize in Physiology or Medicine.

You might be an inventor if ...

In an article that would make Jeff Foxworthy proud, we help you determine if you or your spouse might be an inventor.

Ladies, does your husband stay up half the night tinkering in the garage? When you catch him sneaking off to the local hardware store late at night, does he deny working on his latest invention and instead make up some lame excuse ... such as claiming that he was at the bar with the guys?

If so, then he might be an inventor.

Guys, do you notice that your wife's purse seems to be getting bigger every day? By the way, have you ever tried to figure out what some of the items are that she carries in her purse? Chances are, it's more than just makeup and keys. She probably has some prototypes, a copy of *Inventors' Digest* magazine and maybe the business cards of a few good patent attorneys in there.

If so, then she might be an inventor. Since you, as a guy, are not allowed to look into your wife's purse under any circumstances, you have no way of knowing for sure. This story – the ultimate test to determine if you or your spouse might be an inventor – will help you figure it out.

You might be an inventor if ...

💡 You give your pets names such as Patent, Einstein, Da Vinci, Edison, etc. (It was OK for TV's Frasier Crane to name his dog "Pavlov" on *Cheers* because he played a psychiatrist on TV.)

💡 You give your kids names such as Patent, Einstein, Da Vinci, Edison, etc.

💡 You've ever tried to make a radio out of a coconut – because the Professor on *Gilligan's Island* could do it.

You might be an inventor if ...

💡 You believe that Binford Tools, the fictional company on TV's *Home Improvement*, is a real company.

💡 You actually own some Binford tools.

🔅 As a kid, you routinely took apart electrical appliances or engines and tried to put them back together. Add five points if you finished with more parts than you started with.

You might be an inventor if ...

🔅 Your list of "Most Admired People" includes Hollywood inventors such as Major Boothroyd of James Bond fame (also known as Q), the crazy-haired Doc Brown from the *Back to the Future* movies or Rick Moranis's character in *Honey, I Shrunk The Kids*.

🔅 You believe that TV's MacGyver really could make a homemade bomb using only a paper clip and an empty gas can. Deduct five points if you've ever tried to make a homemade bomb using only a paper clip and an empty gas can.

🔅 You go more than 3 months without filing a patent application and the Patent Office calls to see if you're OK.

🔅 The Patent Office's phone number is on your speed dial.

🔅 Your phone number is on the Patent Office's speed dial.

If you think you're an inventor, then you just might become one someday.

#

A special thanks goes out to the author's nephew, 14-year-old Johnny Wood, for his contributions to this story. Johnny plans on taking over Invention Mysteries when Uncle Paul turns 65 in the year 2030.

What do these inventors have in common?

It's time for a short pop quiz, with only one question. So you either get a 100% or a 0%. The pressure's on.

Question: What do the inventors of the following products have in common?

- The first washing machine (1871)
- The first dishwasher (1872)
- The first car heater (1893)
- The first medical syringe (1899)
- The first windshield wipers (1903)
- The first refrigerator (1914)

Answer: They were all women.

There are many interesting facts about female inventors that you probably don't know. For example, women were not allowed to own property during parts of the 1700's and 1800's. Since patents are considered property, women were not allowed to get patents on their inventions.

For example, Ann Mathews invented a process for cleaning and curing corn in 1715. She is believed to be the first woman whose invention eventually received a patent, although it was granted to her husband. Some inventors applied for patents by using their initials instead of their first names, and it is likely that some of these inventors were women. There were other women besides Ms. Mathews who filed for patents in their husbands' names.

So when did female inventors break through the gender barrier?

Mary Kies is believed to be the first known woman to receive a patent when she patented her process of weaving straw with silk in 1809. Ms. Kies did not receive a patent number for her invention, though, because the Patent Office didn't issue patent numbers until

1836. Approximately 10,000 non-numbered patents were issued prior to 1836, and most of those were lost when a fire destroyed the Patent Office building that year.

The first black woman to receive a U.S. patent was Sarah Goode in 1885. Goode owned a furniture store in Chicago when she patented a cabinet bed.

In 1890, fewer than one percent of U.S. patents were issued to women. By 2002, that number had risen to fifteen percent.

In 1991, Gertrude Elion became the first woman inducted into the National Inventors Hall of Fame, which is located in Akron, Ohio. Elion and her colleague George Hitchings created drugs to fight leukemia, gout, malaria, herpes and AIDS. Altogether, she was involved with 45 patents and was awarded the Nobel Prize in Medicine in 1988.

Ms. Elion wasn't the first woman to win a Nobel Prize, though. That honor went to Marie Curie in 1903. It was another woman, Bertha von Suttner, who helped convince Alfred Nobel to establish a Nobel Prize for Peace, which she won in 1905. Altogether, 31 women have won the various Prizes since they were established in 1901.

It probably comes as no surprise that women invented the first washing machine and the first dishwasher since women did nearly all of the housework in those days, but women also invented fire escapes, laser printers, Liquid Paper®, Scotchgard®· the COBOL computer language, and the Kevlar® used in bulletproof vests just to name a few.

Who was it who told me that in 1890 fewer than one percent of U.S. patents were issued to women?

The editor of *Inventors' Digest* magazine who – you guessed it – is a woman.

Despite his unusual name,
Herbert The Inventor achieved great success

All right, before I get a bunch of hate mail from all the Herberts in the audience, let me explain that it wasn't the inventor's real name that was unusual. It was his nickname that was a bit odd. I'd like to reveal his nickname to you at this point in the story, but that would give away the ending, so I've sprinkled some hints throughout the story instead.

Herbert was born in New York in 1901 as the youngest of five brothers who would eventually "go west" to pursue their careers. The three oldest brothers were very involved in the family business while Herbert only dabbled in it. His next-oldest brother, Milton, worked in women's clothing for a while. No, he didn't wear women's clothing, but he worked as a dressmaker before joining his brothers in a behind-the-scenes type of role. That's enough monkey business about his brothers; let's get back to Herbert's career.

Herbert had several jobs over the years, including that of a horse breeder (the brothers preferred a day at the races over a night at the opera), a grapefruit grower, a commercial fisherman and an inventor. Did Herbert have much of an impact as an inventor? You bet your life he did. It is also a role which very few people know anything about.

He created two inventions which were significant, for better or worse: a wristwatch for cardiac patients and a clamping device that was used in World War II. His wristwatch for cardiac patients had an alarm that went off every time it detected an irregular heartbeat. The inspiration for this device came from a friend who had this condition.

Herbert sold thousands of his patented wristwatch invention, and it probably saved some lives, but his next invention helped end thousands of lives. It ended the war as well. Known as the Marman clamp, it was used to strap down the atomic bombs aboard the airplane that dropped them in Nagasaki and Hiroshima.

It wasn't his career as an inventor which earned Herbert his fame and popularity, but rather his career as an entertainer. His unusual nickname may have given him some notoriety in this career. Herbert worked with his brothers in his first career; in fact, his famous older brother, Julius, once claimed that Herbert was the most talented of all the brothers. Herbert grew tired of that business, though, and gave it up despite the opportunity it offered him.

You see, unusual nicknames were common in Herbert's family. If you want proof, you can check with his brothers Leonard, Adolph, Julius and Milton, who were also known as: Chico, Harpo, Groucho and Gummo.

It was the youngest brother, Herbert – the "Fifth Marx Brother" – who invented both the wristwatch for cardiac patients and the clamping device used in World War II. You probably remember him as Zeppo.

I mentioned earlier that there are some hints spread throughout this story. If you go back and read it again, you'll find the names of some of the Marx Brothers' movies, including: *Go West, Monkey Business, A Day at the Races* and *A Night at the Opera.* There's also the Groucho Marx television show, *You Bet Your Life* that was mentioned earlier.

Inventors' quirks lead to the pursuit of worthless trivia

A common myth about inventors is that they stay up all hours of the night working in their garages. Another myth is that they are eccentric and have crazy frazzled hair. While these aren't very accurate descriptions, a number of inventors had quirks that made them very interesting, maybe even peculiar. You be the judge.

Some of these little nuggets of trivia appeared in previous stories, so think of this story as a highlight film. Or, better yet, a bloopers reel. Best of all, it's better than anything a person could make up.

We begin with some aviation trivia ...

☀ The inventors of the first manned airplane, Wilbur and Orville Wright, never received their pilots' licenses.

☀ In case you're wondering, Glenn Curtiss was assigned pilot's license # 1 and the inventor of the modern folding parachute, Captain Tom Baldwin, was assigned pilot's license # 7.

☀ The "black box" flight recorders found in commercial airplanes are actually orange.

Even the most well-known inventors can't hide from their quirks ...

☀ Even though Walt Disney "invented" Mickey Mouse, he was afraid of ... mice!

☀ One of the greatest visionaries and inventors of all time, left-handed Leonardo da Vinci, recorded his inventions and discoveries in his notebooks by writing backwards, from right to left. Some people believe that he did this in order to prevent others from copying his ideas, but that's probably not true because his writings could easily be deciphered with a mirror.

🔆 A teacher sent little 6-year-old Tommy Edison home from school one day with a note stating, "He is too stupid to learn." At the age of sixteen, he created his first invention, an "automatic repeater," which transmitted telegraph signals between unmanned telegraph stations.

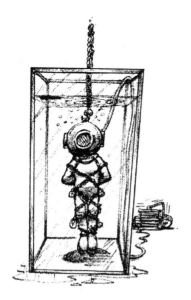

🔆 Magician Harry Houdini, who invented and patented a diver's suit in 1921, was claustrophobic. Who'd a thunk it? Actually, this makes sense when you realize that his diver's suit invention was intended to allow a deep-sea diver to remove the suit by himself if he was in danger.

🔆 Alexander Graham Bell fought off more than 600 lawsuits over his telephone patent. He won all but two of them, and they were both over minor issues.

Since no bloopers story would be complete without government officials, we honor ...

🔆 Former patent commissioner Charles Duell, who in 1899 supposedly remarked that "Everything that can be invented – has already been invented."

🔆 Thomas Jefferson, our nation's most accomplished Presidential inventor, did not patent any of his own inventions. He incorrectly believed that patents deprived people of the benefits that come with new inventions.

🔆 Jefferson apparently changed his mind about patents because he later helped establish the U.S. Patent Office and became the first patent commissioner.

☀ The inventor of the World Wide Web, Tim Berners-Lee, could have patented it and probably become the wealthiest man alive (I'll try to resist the urge to make an Al Gore comment here). Instead he chose not to patent it so that the Web could reach its full potential. If he had patented the Web, he probably would have faced 600 lawsuits from imposters claiming that they invented it. See Alexander Graham Bell above.

Finally, there's even some trivia about people whose invention-related roles were misunderstood or just plain unknown throughout history ...

☀ Rube Goldberg's claim to fame resulted from his cartoons depicting ten or more steps to achieve a simple task. Yet this man, whose name is synonymous with inventions, never invented anything in his life.

☀ Alfred Nobel, the man who created the five Nobel Prizes, is also the inventor of ... dynamite.

In case you haven't had enough worthless trivia yet, here's one more for you: The orange black box flight recorders mentioned earlier were invented in Australia. Now you've had enough.

In the shadow of a genius
lies a brilliant woman

This isn't the rare story about a man who was overshadowed by his wife. It's the tragic story of a woman overshadowed by her husband. Most people have never heard of her, but everyone knows his name.

Her name was Mileva Maric, and she was born in 1875 near Zagreb, in what is now Croatia. She was born with a birth defect that was common in her region, and it caused her to walk with a limp all throughout her life.

Mileva was a successful, self-made woman who gave up a promising career to help her husband pursue his career. She was a few years younger than Marie Curie, and the two met later in life. She might have been on a par with Curie if she had pursued her own career. Her story remains mostly unknown to this day, even to historians.

When Mileva was 20, she began studying medicine at a university in Zurich, one of the few universities at the time that admitted women. This is where she met her future husband, who was three years younger than she. We'll call him Al until his full name is revealed. Al was a Jewish boy from Munich, Germany.

Both Mileva and Al failed their final exams at the university, probably as a result of spending too much time together and not enough time studying. (Parents, feel free to use this story to lecture your kids on what will happen to them if they don't study.)

Al later received a diploma, but Mileva did not. When Al was the only person in his class to not receive a teaching offer, he went to work at the Swiss Patent Office. It was while working at the Patent Office that he became a household name, albeit not for patenting any of his inventions.

Al's parents disapproved of the relationship from the beginning. For one reason, Mileva and Al were of different faiths. To make matters worse, she became pregnant out of wedlock with his child. Worse yet, her parents disapproved of the relationship, too.

After losing their daughter, Lieserl, to an early death, the couple had two sons, Hans and Eduard. They had a breakthrough year in 1905 when Al had three of his scientific papers published. The third one was entitled, *On the Electrodynamics of Moving Bodies.*

Their marriage was turbulent at times, and they divorced in 1918 after 16 years of marriage. Al later married again, this time to his cousin Elsa, only to have that marriage end in divorce, too.

Things didn't turn out any better for Mileva. In 1920 she moved back home to help her ill parents, but she also had to care for her sister who was suffering from psychological problems. Her sister once burned a large sum of cash, literally, that was hidden in an empty stove. (Again, parents, feel free to use this story to lecture your kids on what can happen if they hide their cash in the stove.)

As for Al's "On the Electrodynamics of Moving Bodies" paper mentioned earlier, you probably know it by its other name ... *Einstein's Theory of Relativity.* Albert went on to win the Nobel Prize in Physics in 1921.

You knew all along that it was Albert Einstein, didn't you?

Mileva spent the last years of her life caring for their son, Eduard, who was suffering from schizophrenia. While Albert was not a very good husband, he was an even worse father. He immigrated to America in 1933 and never saw Eduard or Mileva again, even though Eduard lived another 32 years.

When Mileva died in 1948, her obituary made no mention of Albert. A hidden collection of love letters that Albert and Mileva had written to each other in their early years together was made public in 1990, finally revealing the extent to which Mileva contributed to Albert Einstein's success.

Which presidents are better inventors: Republicans or Democrats?

The Political Division of Invention Mysteries World Headquarters has issued its official position regarding presidential inventors.

Several U.S. presidents were inventors before they moved into the White House, so we take a look at how this could influence the election results. With my loyal and bipartisan dog, Patent, watching over me to make sure that I score this contest accurately, we've devised a system that's fair to both parties.

Votes will be awarded as follows:

💡 1 vote for a patented invention, even if it fails in the market-place

💡 2 votes for an invention that succeeds in the marketplace, whether patented or not

💡 3 votes for a patented invention that succeeds in the market-place

💡 Any number of votes will be deducted for any acts that are "unbecoming of a president."

In chronological order, we begin with Thomas Jefferson, who was by far the greatest presidential inventor in U.S. history. Jefferson created at least nine successful inventions, including: a moldboard plow, a wheel cipher, a spherical sundial, a portable copying press, automatic double doors, the bookstand, the swivel chair, the dumbwaiter and a macaroni machine. That's 18 votes if you're keeping score at home. He also introduced French fries, ice cream, waffles, and macaroni to the U.S.

Abe Lincoln invented a solution to help him navigate a boat through shallow waters while he was an Illinois Congressman. He was issued Patent # 6,469 for "A Device for Buoying Vessels Over Shoals" in 1849. Lincoln never commercialized his invention, but he made a wooden model of it which sits in the Smithsonian Institution. Score two points for Lincoln's Republican Party.

Even though Lincoln's successor, Andrew Johnson, didn't invent the process of impeachment, he was the first U.S. president to actually be impeached (he was impeached by the House but acquitted by one vote in the Senate). Deduct three votes, but for which party? Johnson was both a Democrat and a Republican during his career, so his negative votes get thrown out.

Enter another Republican president, Rutherford B. Hayes. President Hayes was not an inventor, but we deduct two votes from his party under the "Acts Unbecoming of a President" clause instituted at the beginning of this column. Some might even say that Hayes's offense, like Johnson's, was an impeachable one. What was his crime?

Upon seeing a demonstration of Alexander Graham Bell's telephone in 1876, Hayes failed to realize its benefits at first. He remarked, *"That's an amazing invention, but who would ever want to use one of them?"* By the way, the "B" in his middle name stands for "Birchard."

Another Republican, Teddy Roosevelt, gets two votes for the teddy bear that bears his name. Roosevelt didn't patent the teddy bear because he's not the one who created it. It was invented by Morris Michtom, who named it after the president and presented it to him as a gift in 1903.

Deduct three votes for the Republican Party for Richard Nixon's impeachment proceedings and subsequent resignation. His negative votes get cancelled out by Democrat Bill Clinton's impeachment, though.

So there you have it – the entire 215-year history of presidential inventions in a nutshell. Now it's time to count up the votes to see which party will occupy the White House for the next four years. Drumroll, please.

The votes are in, and it doesn't look good for either party. The Republicans, with Lincoln, Hayes, Roosevelt and Nixon, have minus one vote, while the Democrats have minus three votes because of Clinton's impeachment. This means that Thomas Jefferson's party is the winner. To which party did Jefferson belong?

He was a member of – and I'm not making this up – the "Democratic-Republican Party." When Jefferson was first elected in 1801, the nation didn't have the same two-party system that it has today. There were additional political parties during the 1800's, such as the Federalists and the Whigs.

I think we need a re-count.

Fire at U.S. Patent Office destroys nearly all patent records

Now that I have your attention, let me explain what happened. The fire that destroyed the Patent Office happened in 1836.

What makes it interesting is the events surrounding the fire.

The Patent Office was housed in the same Washington, DC building as the fire department and the post office. The building was known as Blodgett's Hotel. On cold days, people would burn firewood to heat the buildings. In order to reduce the chance of fire, Patent Office employees stored the wood in the basement. As long as there was nothing to provide a spark, there was little chance of fire.

Unfortunately, the post office clerks in the building also stored ashes in a box in a corner of the fuel room. At 3:00 in the morning of December 15, 1836, ashes spread and ignited the fuel room. This shouldn't have turned into a major fire since the fire department was in the same building, but the fire hose was sixteen years old and in such bad shape that it was useless, but no one found out until they had to use it the night of the fire.

The fire destroyed all 10,000 patents and a few thousand patent models. At the time, the Patent Office didn't number the patents, but it did require each inventor to submit a working model of his invention. Eventually more than 2,800 of the patent files were recovered. These were then given a number beginning with the letter X. The patents that were never recovered were cancelled.

Ironically, the Patent Office was located in this building only temporarily because a new, fireproof building was being built when the fire occurred.

The Great Fire of 1836 caused the Patent Office to begin numbering all new patents. Today, most patented consumer products have their patent numbers printed on the packaging or on the actual product. The Patent Office issues more than 100,000 patents each year, and it recently issued Patent # 6,700,000.

History sometimes repeats itself. I said, History sometimes repeats itself. In 1877, a second fire occurred at the Patent Office. By now the office was in the new "fireproof" building that was being built when the 1836 fire occurred. The 1877 fire caused much more damage than the 1836 fire did, but no patents were lost this time because the office had begun the practice of making copies of each new patent filing.

Here are a few other details that you might not know about patents:

🔅 The very first patent issued in the United States went to Samuel Hopkins of Vermont for his method of making potash. The fee was only $4! Today, patent fees start at approximately $4,000.

🔅 After the 1836 fire, John Ruggles received U.S. Patent # 1 for his invention of traction wheels.

🔅 The first patent in the world was issued to architect Filippo Brunelleschi of Florence, Italy, for his method of transporting goods up a river in 1421.

☼ The first known female patent holder in the U.S. was Mary Kies for her process of weaving straw with silk in 1809. Women were not allowed to own property, including patents, during parts of the 1700's and early 1800's.

☼ In 1890, fewer than one percent of U.S. patents were issued to women. Today, women account for fifteen percent of the more than 100,000 utility patents issued to individual inventors each year.

☼ Thomas Jennings became the first black man to receive a patent in 1821, and he used some of the earnings from his patent to purchase his family out of slavery.

Did the Amish invent the horse saddle?

"The outside of a horse is good for the inside of a man" ... Anonymous

As regular readers of *Invention Mysteries* know, I live on a horse farm just south of Quincy, Illinois. I recently took my horse, a black 3-year-old gelding named Bocephus (hey, a cool horse must have a cool name), to an Amish man in Missouri to break him.

To break a horse means to train it to accept a rider. I gave up trying to break horses in 1988 when Bocephus' grandfather nearly broke me. That's why we no longer have a horse training division here at Invention Mysteries.

When I noticed the saddle that the Amish man used was a little different from the saddles that we use, it made me wonder who invented the horse saddle. (No, I don't think about inventions 24 hours a day, in case you were wondering.)

But first, let's look at the Amish way of life — a way of life which keeps them separated from the outside world.

The Amish were founded by Jakob Amman in Switzerland in 1693, and they began immigrating to America in the late 1800's and early 1900's. They are one of several Anabaptist groups which also include the Hutterites and Mennonites.

Imagine life without cars, trucks or tractors, with no electricity, televisions, radios, computers or telephones. That's part of the Amish way of life. Visiting this Amish man's farm made me feel like I had just stepped back in time to the mid-1800's.

The Amish make their own clothes and produce much of their own food. They typically don't vote in elections because they believe that God will bring the right person into office. They follow the Bible literally, and attend church services at the home of a different member each Sunday. They speak German in the home, which explains the accent. They learn English when they begin grade school, and their formal schooling ends when they finish grade school.

The Amish people can leave the group once they turn eighteen if they wish, although very few actually do so. Once they get married, they grow beards. The men, that is. Those who violate their religious traditions get excommunicated, or shunned. The Amish live a simple life, but it's a life they choose to live.

Many of the Amish people have their own businesses, which include making cabinets and furniture, running a leather shop, training horses, etc. They didn't invent the horse saddle, though.

People were riding horses as early as 3,000 B.C., long before the Amish came into existence. Prior to the invention of the saddle, riders would use a blanket, just like you've seen the Indians use on TV. Some tribes even rode without bridles, steering the horse by poking it with a whip or a stick that they carried with them.

It's believed that a tribe called the Sarmatians, located near the Black Sea in what is now southern Russia, developed the first saddle in 365 A.D., but it contained neither stirrups nor a horn.

The saddle made it much easier to wage war, for without it the warriors wouldn't have been able to carry weapons or supplies. Attila the Hun's troops rode horses with saddles as they conquered much of Europe during the fifth century A.D.

In fact, it was the Huns who introduced the saddle to Europe. Roughly one thousand years later, the Spanish brought the saddle to America when they arrived by ship in the 1400's.

Spanish cowboys, known as vaqueros, developed what is now known as the Western saddle in the early 1800's. As a result, the Western saddle was first known as the Spanish saddle. The Spanish cowboys added the horn to make it easier for them to lead cattle. Prior to the horn, they would lead cattle by tying a rope onto the horse's tail.

There are two main types of saddles in use today: The Western saddle and the English saddle, or as we say on the farm, a saddle with a horn and a saddle without a horn.

So, to answer the question posed to you in the title of this story: No, the Amish did not invent the horse saddle.

Why were Xerox, Monopoly and Pepsi initially considered failures?

"I think there is a world market for maybe five computers."

Chester Carlson, Charles Darrow and Caleb Bradham. You might not recognize their names, but you know their products.

Chester Carlson

Chester Carlson's working career began early in life, becoming his family's main provider before he started high school. A few years later, Chester was working as a patent clerk for Bell Labs in New York when inspiration struck.

Tired of having to manually retype patent descriptions and redraw patent drawings whenever copies were needed, he set out to devise a method of making photocopies. Chester patented his method in 1937. It took 22 years for him to become an overnight success after teaming up with a small paper manufacturing company named Haloid. The product became known as the Model 914, and Haloid soon changed its name to Xerox.

Where would some of America's largest office products companies like Staples and Kinko's be without Chester Carlson's invention? They would be non-existent.

Despite all of Chester's success, he was rejected at first.

IBM, Kodak, General Electric and nearly twenty other companies rejected his idea.

Charles Darrow

The precursor to Monopoly was a 1904 game called "The Landlord's Game," which taught people the unfairness of realty and tax systems. Soon people were customizing the game to reflect their own neighborhoods. After Charles Darrow of Germantown, Pennsylvania, played one of these games at a friend's house, he changed the game to what became Monopoly and began manufacturing the games himself and selling them for $4 each.

Despite all of Charles' success, he was rejected at first.

Parker Brothers rejected it in a big way, citing 52 fundamental flaws. So Charles did what any determined inventor would do – he continued selling the game himself. When Parker Brothers saw the success Charles was having during the Christmas season of 1934, they agreed to buy the rights from him.

Caleb Bradham

North Carolina native Caleb Bradham created Pepsi in 1893, although it wasn't originally called Pepsi. He named it after himself and called it "Brad's Drink." Caleb Bradham poured a sample of his mixture into a beaker and gave it to his assistant to taste it. When he saw his assistant's face light up upon tasting it, Caleb knew he had created a winner.

He later renamed it Pepsi Cola after its two main ingredients, pepsin and the cola nut. Pepsi Cola was successful until sugar prices went bad in 1923. Eight years later, the Loft Candy Company purchased a bankrupt Pepsi Cola Company.

Despite all of Pepsi's early success, it was rejected at first.

When the Loft Candy Company struggled with Pepsi just like its founder did, they offered to sell it to Coca-Cola. Unfortunately for Coca-Cola, they rejected it without even making a bid.

So the common theme here is ... ?

That's right; each invention was rejected before the world figured out what a great invention it was.

You can't really blame the companies that rejected them, though. Chester Carlson's Xerox technology, with terms like "electrostatics" and "photoconductivity," was so new and so different from anything that had ever been created that no one else understood it.

Monopoly made Charles Darrow the world's first millionaire board game inventor, even though he wasn't the person who designed the original version of the game.

Pepsi, on the other hand, was just one of many cola companies of that era, and its early bankruptcy made it less than an ideal prospect.

From the Department of Useless Trivia, Pepsi spawned the first advertising jingle in history. Called "Nickel Nickel," the jingle also became a hit record.

Who was it who made the quote at the beginning of this column?

Former IBM chairman Thomas Watson, in 1943. And despite all of his success, his comment was rejected at first.

National Gallery recognizes seven award-winning inventors

The patent files include so much technical language that it's practically impossible for anyone to understand them. Patents are written in a foreign language known as lawyer-esque, which is something that only the lawyers can enjoy and understand.

The National Gallery, part of the Partnership for America's Future, recently presented awards to seven outstanding inventors for their work. Here, then, are the seven inventors and their inventions:

🔦 Ms. Hyeyeon Choi of Dix Hills, New York, invented *"The Effect of Superficial Fluids on Polymer Thin Films."*

🔦 Joline Marie Fan of Columbus, Ohio, invented *"Heat Transfer Enhancement of Drag-Reducing Surfactants."*

🔦 Then there's Elena Glassman of Pipersville, Minnesota. She invented the *"Brain-Computer Interface for the Muscularly Disabled."*

🔦 Vaishali Grover of Miami, Florida, invented an *"Environmentally-Friendly Enzyme-Based Anti-Fouling Paint."*

Other than their high-tech capabilities, can you figure out what these award-winning inventors have in common? At first glance it appears that the common denominator is the fact that they're all women.

But then there's Sean Mehra and Jeff Reitman of Jericho, New York, who teamed up to invent a process of *"Using Nanoparticles to Enhance Polymer Properties for Improved Commercial Applications."*

Rounding out these seven award-winning inventors is Chandler Macocha of Oxford, Michigan, who invented the *"Wheelchair Backpack Helper."* Finally, an invention that us non-geniuses can figure out (or would that be non-geniui?).

What was Chandler's problem? Was he inventing with one hand tied behind his back?

Actually, the problem may have been his age, since Chandler was three or four years younger than the other inventors. He was only in the 8th grade, while the others were in the 11th and 12th grades.

For most people, myself included, the words in italics above are just plain hard to understand. Let's take a look at the inventors' backgrounds, which are more interesting than the technical descriptions of their inventions.

Hyeyeon Choi was born in Korea and moved to the United States with her family at age twelve. She's an accomplished violinist, pianist and drummer who plans to study chemical engineering in college and do research after graduation.

Invention seems to run in Joline Marie Fan's family. Her mom is a chemist and her dad teaches chemical engineering. Typical underachieving family! Joline was named after Marie Curie while her brother, Jonathan Albert Fan, was named after Albert Einstein. She plans to become a medical researcher, a surgeon or an engineer.

Elena Glassman first used the family computer when she was only 18 months old. She was inspired to invent her brain-computer interface after seeing a paralyzed man use his hands to pick up objects from a table. Elena plans to follow in her father's footsteps and become an electrical engineer.

Vaishali Grover was only two years old when she learned to read. Now she envisions her anti-fouling paint being used to prevent barnacles from building up on ships. She hopes to become a documentary filmmaker someday.

Best friends Sean Mehra and Jeff Reitman have both been accepted to Yale, where they plan to study medicine. Sean can speak Hindi, Punjabi and French, while Jeff was recently chosen to be the U.S. Ambassador for the Third Asia Pacific Economic Cooperation Youth Science Festival.

Chandler Macocha, who once made a paper model of the *Titanic* for his grandmother, plans to become either a flight director for NASA or an engineer at Disney World.

Each of their inventions is either patented (mildly difficult to do), won a national invention competition (more difficult to do) or is marketed nationwide (most difficult to do). Each one of these young Einsteins achieved this before graduating from high school.

Could one of these young inventors become the next Edison?

In the previous story, we looked at the contributions of several successful young inventors. We stay true to that theme for this next story. While the inventors featured previously were teenage inventors, the six inventors in this week's column hadn't even celebrated their twelfth birthday by the time they achieved some success.

Rich Stachowski invented Water Talkies™ in 1996 when he was just ten years old as part of Wild Planet's Kid Inventor Challenge contest. He formed his own company to make more toys when he saw how popular his invention had become. Wild Planet then acquired Rich's company. Now he can go back to being a kid again.

Young Shannon Crabill invented what she called the "Create-your-own-message-alarm-clock," also as part of Wild Planet's contest. Wild Planet changed the name to "Talk Time." Think that's impressive? Oprah Winfrey sure thought so, and she invited Shannon to be a guest on the show and she also featured her in *Oprah* magazine.

Thanks to ten-year-old Stephanie Mui (that's pronounced "Mui"), it's now easier to remove splinters and ticks. Her invention, called "See and Tweezz," combines an all-in-one magnifying glass, tweezers and light. It even comes with a cute little name. Way to go, Stephanie.

Eleven-year-old Tessanie Marek invented "Easy Crutches." This pair of crutches allows a person to rest his or her foot while walking instead of having to hold it up. How does it work? Easy Crutches contains a pedal that is screwed to the crutch in a way that supports the foot. Very few people are on crutches at any given time, but wouldn't it be great to have the Easy Crutches when you need them?

Then there's eight-year-old Matthew Nettleton, who invented the "Pin Picker." The Pin Picker helps you find and pick up sewing pins that have dropped on the floor. It works on both hard floors and rugs. 'Atta boy, Matthew!

While the Pin Picker might not be for everybody, the next invention is. Eleven-year-old Paul Simmons invented the Anti-Soggy Cereal Bowl. It's a double bowl with springs, and it keeps your

cereal from getting soggy by helping you use just the right amount of milk.

I can see the letters and e-mails pouring in already: "But these aren't life-altering inventions. What's so great about a Pin Picker or an Anti-Soggy Cereal Bowl?"

Since I usually answer critics' questions with an equally annoying question of my own, I ask, "What were some of the more famous inventors doing in their early years?"

Thomas Edison created his first important invention, a telegraphic repeating instrument, while working as a telegraph operator in 1865. He was eighteen at the time. Three years earlier, he had begun publishing a weekly newspaper, which he printed in a freight car that also served as his laboratory.

What about Ben Franklin? While he was Ben Franklin the Inventor, he was also Ben Franklin the Publisher and Ben Franklin the First U.S. Postmaster General. Not to be outdone (by himself), he was also Ben Franklin the Signer of the Declaration of Independence, as well as Ben Franklin the First Person to Appear on a U.S. Postage Stamp.

While you might not recognize the names of these next two inventors, you probably used their inventions when you were a kid.

In 1873, 17-year-old Chester Greenwood applied for a patent for his earmuffs. Nothing significant about that, except that his factory made these earmuffs for the next 60 years, and Greenwood went on to create more than 100 other inventions.

Then there's the story of 16-year-old George Nissen, who built a rectangular frame with a piece of canvas stretched across it in 1930 and called it a trampoline. George had designed it in his parents' garage and built it out of steel materials from a junkyard.

Could any of our six young inventors turn out to be the next Thomas Edison or the next Marie Curie? Who knows? But they're off to a pretty good start if they decide to continue inventing.

Do all successful inventors get the credit (and the wealth) they deserve?

In this story, we take a look at three successful inventors. Actually, only two were inventors, but the work of the other one is nearly as well-known as those of the other two. You'll find out which of these pioneers, if any, received any reward or recognition for their efforts.

Not really a family business ...

During the 1830s, natural rubber had become a big hit, but only for a short while. It melted in hot weather, froze in cold weather and had a tendency to stick to just about everything.

Charles Goodyear conducted his first experiment with rubber while in debtor's prison. In a later experiment, he accidentally spilled some rubber mixed with sulfur on a hot stove. The rest, as you know, is history. Or so it appears.

How did he do personally as a result of his work?

While conducting his experiments, Goodyear was constantly on the verge of being broke – completely broke. During his long years of experimenting with rubber, there were times when he couldn't even feed his children.

Despite being a successful inventor, Goodyear was an unsuccessful businessman who turned down some good deals. Plus, there were the infringers. He fought 32 patents all the way to the Supreme Court, and even when he won, he couldn't stop the infringers. His process of vulcanization was named after Vulcan, the Roman god of fire, but it didn't get that name from Goodyear. It came from a friend of one of his biggest infringers.

Charles Goodyear was $200,000 in debt when he died, but his family lived comfortably from the royalties they later received. And wouldn't his family receive some income from the world's No. 1 tire company that bears his name and rings up more than $13 billion in annual sales?

Actually, the only relationship that the Goodyear Tire and Rubber Company has ever had with the Goodyear family is the name. The company was named in his honor – 38 years after he died.

In 1976, more than 100 years after his death, Charles Goodyear was elected to the Inventors' Hall of Fame.

In a land far, far away ...

Bram Stoker was born in Dublin, Ireland, in 1845. Like me, he had four brothers and two sisters. Unlike me, he was a very sickly boy until age seven or eight, hardly leaving his house during that time. His unusual name came from his father, Abraham.

Bram was not an inventor, but he created something that could be just as valuable to society as an invention — a brilliant piece of literature. He was able to support himself and his writings while working for British actor Sir Henry Irving, who was the first actor to be knighted. Bram's earlier horror stories failed to catch on, and by the time he succeeded with his most successful work, a story about a character named Vlad, he had already died.

According to a book by Bram's great-nephew, Dan Farson, Bram's mother grew up during a cholera epidemic in Dublin in the mid-1800s. She saw many of her neighbors die of this horrible plague. Hearing these stories, combined with the fact that his mother once cut off an intruder's hand with an axe, may have influenced Bram's interest in writing about horror.

So what is Bram Stoker's brilliant piece of literature?

Count Dracula, aka *Vlad the Impaler.* ·

The stories of the creative geniuses profiled in this story are significant in that the originators never benefited from the wealth and recognition that their work generated. Bram's story is significant in another way too. As with the inventors of the TV (Philo Farnsworth), Velcro (George de Maestral) and Xerox (Chester Carlson), you know about Bram's work, but you probably never heard of him before reading this article.

The pen is mightier than the sword ...

Without Johannes Gutenberg, you wouldn't be reading this story, and I wouldn't be able to type it into my computer. Gutenberg invented the printing press around 1450. The major impact of his printing press was that it allowed for movable type, which made books available to the masses. Prior to that, only the privileged few had access to books and to a good education.

So it's Gutenberg whose story has a happy ending, right?

Not really. He died penniless after a business partner stole his printing press, his ink, his paper and his staff.

Top five inventions of the year revealed

Since I cover the interesting world in which inventors work, I see plenty of unique inventions every week. Many of America's biggest and best companies began with a single product – created by an inventive person who had a good idea and pursued it. Companies like Xerox, Coca-Cola, Nike, Goodyear, Kodak, IBM, etc., were each founded with one single product or invention.

Invention Mysteries reveals five of the best recent inventions that were created by individual inventors, meaning that you're likely to see them on the market soon. You won't see the names of any big companies behind these inventions, because they were invented by individuals. These inventions are totally different from anything that's been invented before, and it's my guess that each one will do very well in the marketplace.

Inventors live in your town and in your neighborhood. The typical inventor can be your next-door neighbor, your co-worker, your sister-in-law or a former classmate. Here, then, are five top inventions that will make you say, "Wow! Why didn't I think of that?"

The Portable Water Sterlizer is a pen-shaped device that zaps harmful bacteria and other microorganisms in drinking water. The lab-certified Water Sterilizer's inventor, Helmut Froeber, is a retired engineer from Irvine, California. He told me that the Water Sterilizer is ideal for campers, the military, travelers and anyone who doesn't have access to clean drinking water. The people who need it the most, though, are those who live in third-world countries. More than one billion people worldwide live without clean drinking water, according to Froeber.

The Safety Egg is a revolutionary child safety seat. This egg-shaped device rolls over on its axis like a Ferris Wheel to absorb the impact of a head-on collision, and it rolls over sideways on its axis during a side-angle collision. The Safety Egg's inventor is self-described "tinkerer" John Guenther of Chicago, who says, "Each year there are 200 deaths and 20,000 injuries because of the shortcoming in car seat design. Car seats were introduced to the market about 25 years ago, and they haven't changed much since then."

The Kitchen Magician is the latest brainchild of a father of two, Ken Tarlow, Founder of America Invents, in San Francisco. Nicknamed the "Swiss Army Knife for kitchen utensils" by Tarlow, it uses hidden-compartment design to conceal its 20 individual utensils, including a knife, spatula, roasting fork, basting brush, etc. It's ideal for apartment dwellers, the military, boy scouts and, of course, kids who are away at college. Of these five award-winning inventors, Ken probably has the coolest job of all, as he has also designed more than 400 products for clients such as Ron Popeil (Ronco) and The Sharper Image.

The Emergency Light Blanket protects motorists when they have to change a flat tire or when they have engine trouble. The Blanket, with its flashing arrows built into it, attaches to the back of any car or truck and signals oncoming motorists to go around you. It is highly visible during the daytime, and its bright L.E.D.  lights can be seen from miles away at night. People have been changing flat tires along the road since — well, since cars were first invented — but it's taken more than 100 years for someone to invent this product. Inventor Pepper Aasgaard of Omaha told me that his wife inspired him to invent it after he saw an accident on the way home from a University of Nebraska football game. The Emergency Light Blanket could have prevented that accident.

The Enter-Trainer Exercise Device is a "heart monitor which controls entertainment devices," according to its inventor, 45-year-old father of three, Joe Volpe of Philadelphia. This nifty little electronic gadget turns any treadmill, exercise bike, etc., into a virtual power generator for the TV, stereo, and video game devices. The best part of this story is the fact that the idea for the EnterTrainer came from — and I'm not making this up — the episode of *Gilligan's Island* in which the Professor made a bike that powered the radio. It's okay to admit that you remember that episode; we all do.

Did the inventor of the metal detector cause a man to die?

James was shot on the night of July 2, 1881, a mere four months after taking an important new job. He lived another 2 fi months after being shot, and he might have survived if the doctors had not tried to save his life. They may have unknowingly caused his death with their efforts to save him.

At the time of his death, he had begun to reform the U.S. postal system, but he didn't work for the postal office.

A father of seven children, James was a former president of a college in his home state of Ohio. I guess there were probably some people who called him, "President James."

In their attempts to save his life, doctors had probed James' body with their fingers and medical instruments while searching for the bullet. This probably caused more damage than the bullet did, as sterilization was not a common practice at the time. One doctor even punctured James' liver while searching for the bullet.

They brought in a man named Alex to help. Alex built an "induction-balance electrical device," which was the world's first metal detector, in an attempt to locate the bullet and save James' life. The device consisted of two electromagnets connected to a telephone receiver and would make a noise when a metal object would pass in between the magnets. Alex had some success with an earlier invention, but this new metal detector, along with the doctors, probably did more harm than good.

When Alex scanned James' body with his metal detector, he heard a faint buzzing noise. Everyone assumed they had found the location of the bullet, and that it was much further in James' body than they had originally thought.

As James' condition continued to deteriorate, the doctors decided to operate in order to find and remove the bullet. The infection grew much worse as the doctors searched for the bullet, and James soon died. They never did find the bullet.

They found that it wasn't the bullet that caused the buzzing noise, but rather the metal springs of James' bed! Metal springs for beds had just been invented, and James was one of the first people to have this new type of bed.

During the autopsy, the bullet was found to be four inches from the spine, in a place that would have allowed James to live, if only the doctors had not tried to save him!

If you haven't figured out the identities of Alex and James at this point, it's because there are a few details that I may have left out earlier in this story. For example, James was elected to the Senate in 1880, but he turned down that job — for a better one!

Just who was this Alex, the inventor of the first metal detector?

I gave you a clue when I said that he had some success with an earlier invention, and that his metal detector involved a telephone receiver. "Alex" was Alexander Graham Bell. You knew that all along, didn't you?

Then who was James, and what job would cause him to turn down a job as a senator?

"James" was James Garfield, and the job was that of United States President. James Garfield became our nation's 20th president when he was elected in 1880.

Take the final invention quiz of this book

The answers can be found in previous stories throughout this book, and at the end of this chapter as well. Grading is as follows:

A = 13 – 15 correct
B = 10 – 12 correct
C = 7 – 9 correct
D = 4 – 6 correct
F = 0 – 3 correct

1. Which of the following inventions have been issued U.S. patents:
   A) A pet petter
   B) A Santa Claus detector
   C) A motorized ice cream cone
   D) All of the above

2. Which well-known inventor electrocuted animals – ranging in size from a dog to an elephant – to try to convince the public that AC electricity was more dangerous than his own DC electricity? HINT: He was featured in a previous quiz in this book.

3. This Swedish chemist and inventor earned the nickname of "The Merchant of Death" when one of his factories blew up in 1864, but he also established a set of five well-known awards named after him. Name the inventor and his invention.

4. Which of the following inventors, if any, have had their images appear on a U.S. postage stamp?
   A) Thomas Edison
   B) Nikola Tesla
   C) Alfred Nobel
   D) Ben Franklin
   E) All of the above

5. You've heard the story of the Pet Rock, but do you know who invented it?

6. What do the following products have in common: The first washing machine (1871); the first dishwasher (1872); the first

car heater (1893); the first medical syringe (1899); the first windshield wipers (1903); the first refrigerator (1914)?

7. *TRUE or FALSE:* The great Missouri inventor George Washington Carver, who invented hundreds of uses for plants, was born to slave parents.

8. Possible trick question #1: Who invented the Archimedes screw?

9. Originally known as Sam, this Missouri inventor was better known for his writings than for his inventions. He showed his high appreciation for inventors when he said, *"Inventors are the creators of the world – after God."* Who was he?

10. Which Croatian-born inventor was the main inventor of both radio and alternating current (AC) electricity, even though many people have never heard of him?

11. Possible trick question #2: Who invented the outboard motor?
A) Evinrude
B) Binford
C) Outboard
D) None of the above; it's still being determined by the courts.

12. What was the job title of the inventor of the vacuum, Otto Von Guericke of Madgeburg, Germany, from 1646 to 1676?
A) Burgermeister
B) Court jester
C) Police chief
D) Historian
E) None of the above; Otto was too busy vacuuming to hold a full-time job.

13. *TRUE or FALSE:* Nancy Johnson developed the first hand-crank ice cream maker in 1847. It was known as the "Johnson Patent Ice-Cream Freezer."

14. Third and final possible trick question: *TRUE or FALSE:* The inventor of the Fahrenheit scale was a man whose last name was Fahrenheit.

15. Which Marx brother was also a successful inventor?

A) Leonard (Chico)
B) Adolph (Harpo)
C) Julius (Groucho)
D) Milton (Gummo)
E) Herbert (Zeppo)

... And the correct answers are:

1. All of the above

2. Thomas Edison

3. Alfred Nobel and dynamite

4. E) All of the above

5. Gary Dahl

6. They were all invented by women

7. TRUE

8. Archimedes. He was a famous Greek mathematician and inventor born during the third century B.C. He also coined the word "Eureka."

9. Mark Twain

10. Nikola Tesla

11. A) Evinrude

12. A) Burgermeister (another term for "mayor")

13. TRUE

14. TRUE

15. E) Herbert (Zeppo)

Eleven-year-old girl's broken crayons lead to new company

When most kids reach for their crayons and find that most of them are broken, they usually accept that there's nothing they can do about it. But not 11-year-old Cassidy Goldstein; when she had a school assignment that required her to use her (mostly broken) crayons, she thought of a clever solution.

Cassidy decided to invent something that would hold her broken crayons and allow her to use them. Do you remember the chalk holder that your grade school teacher would use when her chalk got too short to use effectively? That's similar to Cassidy's Crayon Holder.

In the past, this is the point at which most kids would stop. They invent something that solves a common problem, and then they forget about it. What would you do? Would you know how to manufacture and sell an invention, especially if you were a child?

Fortunately, Cassidy had someone to help her. His name was Norm or, as she called him, Dad. Norm Goldstein was an executive in charge of patented technology with the company that produced Priceline.com, and before that he worked with the top people at The Sharper Image, so he knew how to take a product from concept to reality.

Cassidy's invention led her Dad to start a new company, called By Kids For Kids. Formed in 2003, the company commercializes products that were invented by kids, for kids. Hence, the name. (That's the last time I'll use the word "hence" in this book, I promise.)

Wal-Mart has just placed their second order for the Crayon Holder, and it is also being sold in catalogs. In addition, there are many other products that By Kids For Kids has brought to the market.

Needle Beetle is the brainchild of nine-year-old Brandon Whale. It is a soft, squeezable, beetle-shaped ball that make a kid's veins pop up when receiving a shot, just by squeezing it. It makes it easier for the nurse to locate a vein — avoiding multiple jabs — and also helps take the child's mind off the painful needle.

The Needle Beetle is manufactured by Mattel and was distributed to 180 children's hospitals free of charge this past summer. Brandon was even featured on the Discovery Kids TV show. How cool!

Brandon isn't the only inventor in his family, either. Little brother Spencer invented the Kid Care Riding Toy. This clever device attaches the IV pole (or oxygen tank) to the Riding Toy, meaning that a parent no longer has to chase their kids everywhere out of fear that the needle might come out of the child.

It is ideal for kids receiving an IV or a chemotherapy treatment, and it is selling to children's hospitals all over the US. It is produced by the Little Tykes Company and manufactured by Rand International. Spencer Whale was only six years old when he invented the Kid Care, and he also won several awards for his invention.

Adult celebrities aren't the only ones writing books these days. Twenty-year-old Freddie Zeiler wrote *A Kid's Guide to Giving* when she was just fourteen. The book is published by a company called Innovative Kids. *A Kid's Guide to Giving* will be in bookstores next September.

Large corporations have taken notice of By Kids For Kids – the company that was started with an 11-year-old's crayon holder. So far, Xerox, Mattel and Scholastic have all signed on as sponsors

They've produced the Inventive Thinking Toolkit for Kids, which has been sent to tens of thousands of teachers in grades 3 – 8, as well as distributing it to libraries. The Toolkits are based on the U.S. Patent Office's Project XL, which was designed to teach critical thinking skills to kids.

If you're a teacher or librarian, you can download the By Kids For Kids curriculum from their web site for free. The web address is www.bkfk.com. You might just find something in it that you can use to help develop a future genius – one that you never knew you had in your class.

Have you ever invented anything?

If you have, then here are 5 great places to turn to for help:

☀ By Kids For Kids: If you would like to expand your children's inventive abilities, the By Kids For Kids company has materials that inspires kids and helps them to develop their creative abilities. If you're a teacher or librarian, you can download the By Kids For Kids curriculum for free from their web site. The company also commercializes kids' inventions for them on a percentage basis. www.bkfk.com

☀ *Inventors' Digest* magazine: The "magazine for idea people." www.InventorsDigest.com

☀ MarketLaunchers.com: The "yellow pages of inventions," MarketLaunchers.com builds web pages for inventors and also offers a free online newsletter. Run by Paul Niemann, author of *Invention Mysteries*: www.MarketLaunchers.com

☀ United Inventors Association of the USA: The UIA is a non-profit corporation formed in 1990 to provide leadership, support, and services to inventor support groups and independent inventors. www.uiausa.org

☀ United States Patent Office web site: www.uspto.gov/go/kids/

Bibliography

Clarke, Donald. *The How It Works Encyclopedia of Great Inventors and Discoveries.* Marshall Cavendish Books Limited, London, England, 1978

Hornsby, Jeremy. *The Story of Inventions.* Crescent Books, London, England, 1977

How Was It Done? The Story of Human Ingenuity through the Ages. Reader's Digest, Pleasantville, New York, 1998

Flatow, Ira. *They All Laughed.* HarperCollins, New York, 1992

Freeman, Allyn and Golden, Bob. *Why Didn't I Think of That?* John Wiley & Sons, New York, 1997

Barach, Arnold B. *Famous American Trademarks.* Public Affairs Press, Washington, D.C., 1971

Petroski, Henry. *The Evolution of Useful Things.* Alfred A. Knopf, New York, 1993

Brown, David E. *Inventing Modern America: From the Microwave to the Mouse.* The MIT Press, Cambridge, MA & London, England. 2002

Aaseng, Nathan. *Black Inventors.* Facts On File, Inc., New York, 1997

Williams, Trevor I. *The History of Invention: From Stone Age to Silicon Chips.* Facts On File Publications, New York & Oxford, England, 1987

Bourne, Russell. *The Smithsonian Book of Invention.* Smithsonian Exposition Books, Washington, D.C., 1978

Jones, Charlotte Foltz. *Mistakes That Worked.* Doubleday Dell Publishing Group, Inc., New York, 1991

Inventive Genius: Library of Curious and Unusual Facts. Time-Life Books, Alexandria, VA 1991

Inventors and Discoverers; Changing Our World. National Geographic Society, Washington, D.C., 1971

Adamson, Joe. *Groucho, Harpo, Chico and sometimes Zeppo.* Simon & Schuster, New York, 1973

Niemann, Paul. *Invention Mysteries: The Little-Known Stories Behind Well-Known Inventions.* Horsefeathers Publishing, Quincy, IL, 2004

Microsoft ® Encarta ® 97 Encyclopedia

The Expanded Columbia Electronic Encyclopedia Copyright © 2003.

Inventors' Digest magazine, Boston, MA

The 2003 World Almanac and Book of Facts

Web sites:

Celebrate Black History Month with these inventors

http://inventors.about.com/library/inventors/blkidprimer6_12aa.htm

http://inventors.about.com/library/inventors/blblackhistorymonth.htm

http://inventors.about.com/library/weekly/aa020600i.htm

http://inventors.about.com/library/inventors/blgolf.htm

http://www.uh.edu/engines/epi665.htm

http://www.blackinventionsmuseum.com/newsletter.html

http://www.invent.org/hall_of_fame/38.html

www.african-american-inventors

http://tm.wc.ask.com

Four inventors signed the Declaration of Independence:

www.rebelswithavision.com/GeorgeClymer.com

www.ushistory.org/declaration/signers/hopkinson.htm

www.historychannel.com/exhibits/declaration/bios.html

http://americanhistory.about.com/library/weekly/aa040202a.htm

http://foxpawpress.com/Printshop/museum/privatepress/wayzgoose/chi-wayz/chigoose1/chigoose1.html

Did bootleggers help invent NASCAR?

http://www.decadesofracing.net/TheBeginning.htm

http://www.pittsburghlive.com/x/tribune-review/news/s_183864.html —

www.nascar-info.net

www.SignOnSandiego.com

Charles never received much recognition for his life-saving invention

www.charleslindbergh.com

Who invented the modern baseball glove?

http://www.baseballlibrary.com/baseballlibrary/excerpts/spitters9.stm

Who were Fahrenheit, Celsius, Doppler and Richter?

www.inventors.about.com

www.who2.com/christiandoppler....

http://www.windows.ucar.edu/tour/link=/people/enlightenment/doppler.html

http://www.wildwildweather.com/radar.htm ...

http://www.enc.org/features/calendar/unit/0,1819,48,00.shtm

www.seismo.unr.edu/ftp/pub/lou...

www.thetech.org/hyper/quakes/g...

http://www.ulearntoday.com/magazine/physics_article1.jsp?FILE=ther-mometer

http://empl.ksc.nasa.gov/Links/timeline/timeline.htm

http://www.sciencetrek.net/fahrenheit.htm

http://www.riverdeep.net/current/2001/11/112601_celsius.jhtml

http://www.timelinescience.org/years/1750.htm

http://www.saskschools.ca/~qvss/grassroots02/chernick/research.htm#Anders Celsius

http://neic.usgs.gov/neis/general/richter.html

Is war the stepmother of invention?

www.kyrene.k12.az.us/schools/brisas/sunda/decade/1940.htm

http://www.cbc.ca/kids/general/the-lab/history-of-invention/default.html

http://www.olive-drab.com/od_mvg_www_jeeps_bantam.php3

http://www.butlercountyhistoricalsociety-pa.org/bantam.html

More wartime inventions that benefit mankind

http://www.invent.org/hall_of_fame/182.html

http://web.mit.edu/invent/iow/mauchly-eckert.html

http://web.mit.edu/invent/iow/fleming.html

http://www.schoolshistory.org.uk/floreyandchain.htm

http://www.chemheritage.org/EducationalServices/pharm/antibiot/read-ings/flocha.htm

http://inventors.about.com/library/inventors/blARPA-DARPA.htm

http://inventors.about.com/library/weekly/aa091598.htm ...

http://www.dei.isep.ipp.pt/docs/arpa—1.html

http://e-training.iatp.md/seminars/digitalmedia/1.html

Which Presidents are better inventors: Republicans or Democrats?

www.americanpresident.org/history/andrewjohnson

www.usa-presidents.info

Inventors' quirks lead to the pursuit of worthless trivia

http://www.takeaquiz.com/category_pages/phobias.html

Despite his unusual name, Herbert The Inventor achieved great success

http://www.leader-press.com/calendar.shtml

http://encyclopedia.thefreedictionary.com/Marx

http://www.dickinsonstate.com/alumninews.asp?ArticleID=393

http://www.anycities.com/lydiaolydia/zeppo.html ...

http://www.marx-brothers.org/living/zeppo.htm

Did the Amish invent the horse saddle?

saddlezone.com/html-top/saddle...

www.cbc.ca/kids/general/the-lab/history-of-invention/saddle.html

http://religiousmovements.lib.virginia.edu/nrms/amish_arch.html

www.historyforkids.org/learn/s...

Fire at U.S. Patent Office destroys nearly all patent records

www.uspto.gov/go/kids/1836fire.htm

www.myoutbox.net/popch30.htm

National Gallery recognizes seven award-winning inventors

www.pafinc.com/gallery/i04.htm

Could one of these young inventors become the next Edison?

www.pafinc.com/genius

The verdict is in on these ridiculous inventions:

www.totallyabsurd.com/archive.htm

Index

EASY ORDER FORM

Online: www.InventionMysteries.com

E-mail: niemann7@aol.com

Phone: (800) 337-5758. Please have your credit card ready.

Mail: Invention Mysteries, P.O. Box 5148, Quincy, IL 62305

Name: _____

Address: _____

City: _____ State: _____ Zip: _____

Telephone: (_____)_____

E-mail: _____

Please indicate quantity:

Invention Mysteries	_____ x $12.95	= $_____
More Invention Mysteries	_____ x $12.95	= $_____
Total:		$_____

(Volume discounts are available for orders of 3 or more books. Call 800-337-5758 for details.)

Sales tax: Illinois residents please add 7.75% tax before adding the shipping charge.

Shipping: $2.95 per order, regardless of how many books you order.

Payment: (Please circle one)

Check: Visa   Master Card   Discover   AMEX

Card number: _____

Name on card: _____

Exp. Date: ___/___